Teacher's Guide and Answer Key

Structural Arithmetic I

Margaret Stern
Toni S. Gould

About the Authors

Margaret B. Stern is a graduate of Wellesley College and has a master's degree from the Bank Street School of Education. She spends much of her time training teachers of children with learning problems, lectures extensively, and conducts workshops throughout the United States and overseas. She has been a special lecturer at many universities, including Teacher's College, Columbia University, New York University, University of Vermont, and New Jersey State Teacher's College. Ms. Stern is coauthor of the *Structural Reading Program.* Her other publications include *Gould-Stern Early Reading Activities, Children Discover Arithmetic,* and the *Structural Arithmetic Program.*

Toni S. Gould has been a reading consultant in New York City for the past thirty-five years. She is co-author of the widely used *Structural Reading Program, Structural Arithmetic Program,* and the books *The Early Years of Childhood* and *Children Discover Reading.* Ms. Gould has taught at Bank Street College of Education, Hunter College, Lehman College, and has conducted workshops for teachers in schools and colleges throughout the United States.

Contents

Structural Arithmetic Materials

Set A

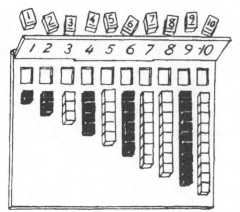

Counting board with number markers 1 to 10,
number guide, and number blocks

Extra number markers and signs

10-box with number blocks

Number boxes 1 to 10

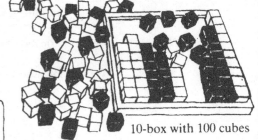

10-box with 100 cubes

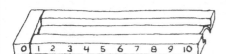

Pattern boards 1 to 10

Set B

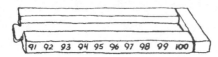

Number track 1 to 100

10-box

4-blocks

3-blocks

2-blocks

Unit cubes

Number blocks 1 to 9 (for multiplication
and division)

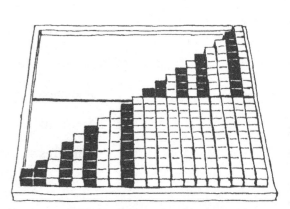

20-tray with number blocks

Introduction

Developing Cognitive Thinking

The goal of the Structural Arithmetic Program is to develop cognitive thinking and an appreciation for the exactness and clarity of mathematics. Arithmetic, a branch of mathematics, can and should be taught from the beginning so as to enable children to think and to reason things out for themselves.

Experiments with the Structural Arithmetic materials form the core of the program. The materials, which are designed to make the structure of the number system visible, enable pupils to discover number concepts and to gain insight into the meaning of each operation: addition, subtraction, multiplication, and division.

Teaching Number Facts in Structurally Related Groups

Teaching number facts by rote and in isolation takes from children the joy of using their minds. Such an approach prevents pupils from developing the ability to think and to reason. Children often figure out an addition fact by counting beads or using rods. Since they learn it in isolation, they miss an opportunity to reason. The Structural Arithmetic Program introduces facts in groups, giving children insight into the characteristic structures common to these facts. This procedure allows children to develop the ability to think mathematically as they figure out for themselves the relationships between the number facts and express the generalization in their own words.

As an example of the Structural Arithmetic approach, let us look at the single fact, $3 + 7 = 10$. Children discover all the combinations that make 10 by fitting combinations of blocks into the 10-box. They reason that if 9 needs 1 to make 10, then 8 needs 2, and 7 needs 3 to make 10. By switching the blocks around, they discover that the order of the addends can be changed without changing the sum. Thus, they grasp the commutative property of addition and can put it to use. This enables them to reason that if $7 + 3 = 10$, then $3 + 7 = 10$. This fact has not been learned in isolation, but has been studied in a context where its relation to the other facts can be seen.

Developing Concepts by Measuring, Not by Counting

When children see an example such as $5 + 4 = \underline{\quad}$ and don't know the answer, they often respond by counting "6, 7, 8, 9." Teachers may assume that encouraging children to count will one day result in their stopping counting and saying, "9." In actuality, each time they see $+ 4$ (as in $6 + 4$ or $9 + 4$), they automatically practice counting. The numbers themselves don't have meaning. For the counting child, 5 plus 4 does not equal 9; it makes 9 by counting. No picture in the child's mind makes the number fact $5 + 4 = 9$ unforgettable. Furthermore, if children count the total incorrectly as 10, they have no certain way to check that result except by another uncertain counting procedure. On the other hand, in Structural Arithmetic, the two addends 5 and 4 actually measure 9 in the number track. It becomes obvious, then, that counting is a senseless rote procedure that prevents children from learning to think or reason.

Developing Spatial Thinking and Reasoning

In Structural Arithmetic, children add together two quantities and measure their total; for instance, the 7-block plus the 3-block measures 10. Working with materials in this way allows children to experiment with ideas and to figure out other relationships. They might take one of the blocks from the total and leave the other one, thus discovering the related subtraction fact $10 - 3 = 7$. Whether they are measuring with blocks or working with patterns of cubes, they are using spatial thinking to help them reason. Each experiment leaves a mental picture that the children can turn around in their minds to explore new relationships.

Progressing from Thinking to Writing Equations

As soon as children want to communicate what they have been thinking spatially, they must put their ideas into words. Teachers should encourage them to use their own phrasing, such as "7 needs 3 to be as big as 10," and "When you take 3 away from 10, 7 is left." The final step, then, is easy—to set down these thoughts in equation form: $7 + 3 = 10$ and $10 - 3 = 7$. Experimenting with the materials has enabled children to comprehend and use the symbols and signs of mathematics to form any equation. They have reached the stage of mastery; they fully understand the operations and can give the answers with confidence.

Economy of Learning—The Result of Transfer

By making the structure of our number system visual, the Structural Arithmetic materials make it possible for children to transfer a newly learned fact to other areas. If they know that $5 + 2 = 7$, they can discover that this fact holds true in any decade by measuring in the number track, $15 + 2 = 17$, $25 + 2 = 27$, or $65 + 2 = 67$. By working with cubes and 10-blocks in the dual board the children can find that what is true for ones is also true for tens, $50 + 20 = 70$. The result is an immense economy in the number of facts that have to be learned.

The Structural Arithmetic Program is designed to help children develop number concepts and arrive at generalizations essential to the understanding of mathematics. To the degree in which they develop their ability to think with numbers, their work will be creative and fulfilling.

Teaching Through Experiments in Small Groups

Learning by Insight

Children learn more effectively when they work together in small groups than when they work alone in workbooks. The Structural Arithmetic experiments and games can be carried out by the class as a whole; however, children will learn more if the class is divided into groups of six to ten children. In a small group everyone has more opportunities to handle the materials and to make their own discoveries. The following suggestion has proved successful in many classrooms. Groups A and B use the materials Monday, Wednesday, and Friday, while Group C works independently. On Tuesday and Thursday the groups switch, giving Group C two days of experimenting, while the others work independently. It is more productive for children to learn through insight and understanding several times a week than to spend five days a week in less meaningful drill.

Learning to Sustain Attention and Think Ahead

This skill is important for every child, but above all for children with attention disorders. Playing a game full of interest heightens these children's excitement and helps them lengthen their span of attention. Once totally involved, they do not just give an answer and retire, but become curious about what the others are going to do. This encourages them to think ahead and plan what they will do when it is their turn.

Discovering Other Ways to Reach a Solution

When children work in a group, they can watch someone else solve a problem in a way quite different from the one they would have used. Such an experience is important as it alerts the young students to new ways of reasoning and of figuring things out for themselves.

Learning to Abide by Rules

Learning to follow rules is difficult for all children, yet they soon realize a game can be fair and fun only when there are rules that everyone respects. This allows them to relax and concentrate on the concepts and the mental computation necessary for playing the game.

Structuring a Game

Group games must be more than interesting: they should be structured to protect pupils on different levels of competence. The rules must not allow those children who most need the practice to be eliminated first. When children realize that a winner's victory is due to chance and not to being smart, many of them take heart. They see that they can expect to win, and this expectation keeps them paying attention until the very end of the game.

Improving Receptive Language

Good comprehension of spoken language is important for all children. When words and phrases seem unfamiliar, they can be clarified by the teacher through concrete demonstrations with the materials. Teachers should simplify directions by breaking them into smaller steps. This also allows the teacher to monitor comprehension at each step and to diagnose children's troubles. Since children enjoy following directions given by their classmates, they listen attentively when children are given roles of leadership. We often recommend that children take the role of teacher, or leader, in these games. When they understand what is expected, they relax and become better able to listen to directions the next time.

Improving Expressive Language

Children who learn to use the language of mathematics accurately are better able to understand and to solve written problems. When they take the role of teacher, an option for every game, they learn to express themselves clearly. In order to tell classmates what to do, they must have the number relationships clearly in mind. They might ask a friend to "Go to the table and get the block that comes before the 10-block." When the friend returns with the 9-block, they know they have stated the command accurately. This ability to use language well is an essential step in the development of mathematical reasoning.

Teaching Children with Learning Disorders

Children with learning disorders who learn mathematics with the Structural Arithmetic materials respond with great joy. Handling the materials allows them to make comparisons and begin to state the results in words that have meaning for them. Thus, the main areas of potential weakness are strengthened, for it is their insufficient language skills and poor memories that cause these children to become frightened and humiliated when they try to learn mathematics by rote. They find it almost impossible to understand numerical relationships through verbal explanations, and yet teachers are seldom trained to present mathematical concepts in a more comprehensible manner.

Strengthening Areas of Weakness

Visual-Perceptual Skills. These skills can be improved by having children reconstruct patterns shown by the blanks of the empty pattern boards. They learn to recognize these patterns of cubes at a glance and then to reproduce them with colored cubes. The pattern boards are fashioned to allow children to check their patterns by placing their cubes into empty blanks on the boards. This means they are checking their visual perceptions against their motor and tactile senses.

Expressive Language. Children who have difficulty understanding the meaning of words have trouble expressing themselves. The materials enable children to learn concepts through actions and then to describe what they have been doing in their own words. They might put together the 3-block and the 7-block in the 10-box and then say "3 and 7 together are just as big as 10." When they shorten this to "3 and 7 are 10," the meaning is already built in. It has become the foundation of their work with symbols.

Respecting the Process of Learning

Those who approach teaching as a set of techniques fail to respect the process of learning that is taking place in children. They are too quickly satisfied with a parroted answer. The point is that the answer should be the result of the children's having figured things out for themselves. Children need time to think.

Teaching Remedial Students—A Few Suggestions

Older students who have been failing in their work with number symbols may have no notion of the concepts that lie behind these symbols. They soon improve when they have an explanation they can see and feel and "hang on to." It is not difficult for the teacher or tutor to take the work described for young children and make it appealing to older children or adults. Many of these pupils were never given this foundation in sensorimotor and visual-perceptual work. The tasks described for younger students can be set up for the older ones to practice in much the same way as they practice basic skills for sports. Pupils can compete with themselves by keeping a chart of the length of time it takes them to fill the 10-box with blocks or to match numbers to pattern boards.

There are several very attractive games for building basic concepts in older children, among them the Snake Game (see page 12) and the Sticker Games (see pages 13 and 32). Children usually gain self-confidence from understanding previously incomprehensible problems and experience pleasure in finding they can think. The result is an understanding and appreciation of the materials and a renewed respect for themselves.

Teaching Children to Write Numbers

There are many ways to help children learn to write numbers (numerals) and letters. Teachers have found the following approaches to be of considerable help. Children who find these skills difficult should be taught through a variety of approaches.

Tracing Numbers

Tracing numbers is the approach used in *Structural Arithmetic I*. Most children have the ability to learn to write numbers by tracing symbols printed in dotted-line form. The starting point of the line should be indicated by a dot, which can be colored green. Some children are helped if the dotted line is accompanied by a small arrow that indicates the direction in which they are to draw the line. This is the model used in this workbook.

Writing numbers in the air before tracing or writing them on paper is good practice. Children find it easier to remember in which direction they should draw each line when they feel it with large movements.

Teachers of children who seem to have different styles of learning should try some of the approaches that follow. They have been used with excellent results.

Using Colors

This technique helps some children. The teacher can show the relationships between the lines in the configuration visually by drawing each part in a different color. For example, make the top half-moon of figure *3* green and the bottom half-moon another color. Children with poor perceptual skills, however, very often cannot perceive the two pieces as parts of a new and different whole. For these children this approach is of little help.

Connecting Dot Patterns

This technique is excellent for children who have poor rote memories. Catherine Stern invented games in which a number is drawn over a pattern of dots.* The dots are in the form of the number patterns the children have studied. The number, when drawn over dots, contains the key to the amount it stands for and helps children remember the name of the numeral.

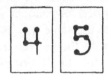

Spacing Figures

Children who write poorly spaced figures are those who have difficulty anticipating the amount of space necessary for a figure and therefore don't know how far over to move after each number to accommodate the next number. The visual motor exercises that follow enable teachers to give children much needed practice in this skill. *Structural Arithmetic I* provides boxes in which the children learn to center each number. This enables them to space their numbers correctly.

Multisensory Approaches for Children Who Need More Work

Motor Skills: The Pencil Grip. The pencil grip must be checked first. The use of a triangular pencil gripper or a ball that fits on the pencil forces the thumb and fingers to learn the proper grip of the pencil.

Motor Skill: Warm-up Exercises. Exercises in relaxation are necessary before special training in small muscle skills.
1. Wet spaghetti: This is a good exercise to help children relax their writing arms. Take the hand of a child in your hand and gently shake it until the arm feels like "wet spaghetti."
2. Making circles with a scarf: Using a necktie or scarf, the children swing big circles above their heads, first clockwise and then counterclockwise. This exercise gets them to relax. In using tiny, cramped writing motions children can't feel what they are doing and tire easily. When the movements are jerky, the scarf will not make a circle, so the teacher must guide children's arms at first. Children soon learn to master an even, rhythmic beat in order to make circle after perfect circle.

Visual-Motor Skills

1. Working with the pattern boards: Children can improve motor and visual perceptual skills by reproducing patterns with cubes. The pattern boards contain patterns of blanks to hold different numbers of cubes from 1 to 10. The children study a pattern, reproduce it with colored cubes, and then place the cubes into the blanks of the board. In this way they check

*Catherine Stern and Margaret Stern, *Children Discover Arithmetic* (New York: Harper & Row, 1971), pp. 67–68.

their visual information with kinesthetic and tactile experiences. The pattern board experiments can be found in *Experimenting with Numbers,* pages 10 to 15.

2. Drawing circles at the chalkboard: Explain to the children that they are going to draw two large circles, using a piece of chalk in each hand. Children face the chalkboard, line up their noses on the chalkboard, and make an *X* there. Explain that *X* is where both hands begin to draw circles, each hand trying to make its own circle "good and big and round." If the children become confused, direct them to concentrate their eyes on the *X*. They soon begin to be able to maintain the focus of their eyes and let their hands work by themselves. This exercise allows them to get important feedback from their bodies.

3. Drawing straight lines at the chalkboard: Some children find it difficult to gauge the length of the line they are going to draw and hard to start and stop when they want to.

a. Drawing lines down

Present these children with two parallel lines drawn on the chalkboard about 4 or 5 inches apart. Children start at the top line, draw a straight line down, and stop at the bottom line. They should learn to guide each motion by chanting to themselves, "Start, stop."

b. Drawing lines left to right

In this exercise, the ladder stands straight up, and the children draw rungs that go from left to right.

c. Long and short lines

In this exercise children draw a long line followed by a short line. They alternate these two lines, chanting "Long, short...." The execution of these strokes is basic to the ability to write the numbers *1, 4, 5,* and *7.*

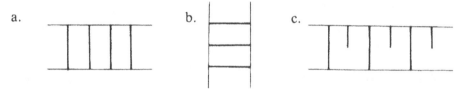

4. Drawing loops at the chalkboard: Make a model by drawing a vertical string of loops. Ask each child to come to the chalkboard and make a similar string of loops. Encourage them to use a relaxed grip on the chalk and to work with a sense of rhythm. Some children may need considerable guidance in making a string of loops. Position them next to the edge of the chalkboard. They need to draw each loop against an edge and to feel that edge in order to know when to stop. Encourage them to dictate to themselves, "Around, stop; around, stop," when they make each loop. When they have mastered this, have them break off and make a figure *3.* Making a string of loops in reverse is good preparation for making the figure *6.* Drawing loops is basic to the writing of figures *2, 3,* and *6.*

Teachers should be aware that motor coordination skills affect self-esteem. Failure is often associated with humiliation. Children's pleasure in functioning well may be reflected in an improved ability to experiment with their hands and eyes and in using the materials around them.

The Structural Arithmetic Program

Preschool and/or Kindergarten

Materials:

Kit A (see inside front cover)

Experimenting with Numbers (teacher's guide)
- contains over 100 experiments with illustrations and easy directions
- sequenced experiments help children advance step by step in their understanding of addition and subtraction

Sequential Development of Concepts

Counting Board and Number Blocks	Pattern Boards and Cubes	The 10-Box and Number Blocks
Level I Children: • work without using number names or symbols • fit blocks into grooves and discover where each block comes in the sequence *Level II* • learn to count to 10, enumerate objects, and give each block its number name • find the number block described by: "one bigger than," "one smaller than," "comes after," "comes before," "comes between," and "is equal to" *Level III* • learn the name of each number symbol from 1 to 10 • learn which number stands for each block • learn that 0 stands for "no block" • learn the meaning of the plus and minus signs	*Level I* Children: • work without using number names or symbols • recognize and match pattern boards with cube patterns 1 to 10 • build the sequence of patterns and know where each pattern comes in the sequence *Level II* • give each pattern its number name • learn about odd and even numbers • name the number that results from: adding or subtracting 0, adding or subtracting 1, adding or subtracting 2 *Level III* • learn which number stands for each pattern • learn the meaning of the plus, minus, and equal signs • demonstrate word problems in addition and subtraction and record them with equations	*Level I* Children: • work without using number names or symbols • fit together combinations of blocks that fill the 10-box *Level II* • know the name of each block and can name the combinations of blocks that fill the 10-box, saying, for instance, "9 needs 1 to make 10," thus discovering the first addition facts • build the stair from 1 to 10 • demonstrate and state the facts that result from adding 1 and adding 2 to each step of the stair *Level III* • learn to use numbers 1 to 10 and the plus, minus, and equal signs to record the addition and subtraction facts discovered in the 10-box • demonstrate addition and subtraction stories and record them with equations • fill number boxes 1 to 9 with blocks • name the combinations that make any number from 1 to 10 • record with number markers the facts from each number box 1 to 10 (see charts on pages 10 and 11)

The Structural Arithmetic Program (continued)

Grade 1

Materials:
Kit A (see inside front cover)
Experimenting with Numbers (see facing page)
Structural Arithmetic I (workbook)
Structural Arithmetic I Teacher's Guide and Answer Key

Sequential Development of Concepts

Children:
- discover addition and subtraction facts with sums of 10 and less
- learn to record these facts
- learn to solve for *x*
- master facts through understanding the characteristics of each structurally related group:
  combinations that make 10
  adding 0, adding to 0
  adding 1, adding to 1
  adding 2, adding to 2
  addition—doubles and neighbors
  difficult facts: 5 + 3, 3 + 5; 6 + 3, 3 + 6
  combinations that make 1 through combinations that make 9
- related subtraction facts for each group (see charts on pages 10 and 11)
- solve word problems using these facts

Grade 2 and Advanced Grade 1

Materials:
Kit B (see inside front cover)
Structural Arithmetic II (workbook)
Structural Arithmetic II Teacher's Guide and Answer Key

Sequential Development of Concepts

Children:
- review facts learned in grade 1
- discover structure of 2-place numbers
- learn to analyze word problems
- learn the value of coins
- learn to tell time and write time
- master facts through understanding the characteristics of each structurally related group:
  adding 9, adding to 9
  adding 8, adding to 8
  combinations that make 11 and 12
  doubles and neighbors (teens)
  related subtraction facts for each group
- transfer facts to higher decades
- build 3-place numbers
- understand regrouping in addition and subtraction

Grade 3

Materials:
Kit B (see inside front cover)
Structural Arithmetic III (workbook)
Structural Arithmetic III Teacher's Guide and Answer Key

Sequential Development of Concepts

Children:
- review 100 basic addition and subtraction facts
- review regrouping in addition and subtraction
- study 3-, 4-, and 5-place numbers
- discover and master the multiplication facts (tables 1 through 12)
- understand the relationship between multiplication and division
- master the basic division facts
- discover division with remainders
- understand the reasons underlying the steps in long division
- analyze problems systematically

Grade 4

Materials:
Kit B (see inside front cover) and fraction materials
Structural Arithmetic IV (workbook)
Structural Arithmetic IV Teacher's Guide and Answer Key

Sequential Development of Concepts

Children:
- study the structure of numbers to 1,000,000
- learn to round off numbers
- study the structure of fractions
- use fraction materials to add, subtract, multiply, and divide fractions
- understand decimal notation
- learn to use decimals in addition, subtraction, multiplication, and division
- understand ratio and proportion
- understand and use percent
- solve problems using these concepts

Basic Addition Facts

	0	1	2	3	4	5	6	7	8	9	10
+0	+0	+0	+0	+0	+0	+0	+0	+0	+0	+0	+0

	0	1	2	3	4	5	6	7	8	9
+1	+1	+1	+1	+1	+1	+1	+1	+1	+1	+1

	0	1	2	3	4	5	6	7	8
+2	+2	+2	+2	+2	+2	+2	+2	+2

	0	1	2	3	4	5	6	7
+3	+3	+3	+3	+3	+3	+3	+3	+3

	0	1	2	3	4	5	6
+4	+4	+4	+4	+4	+4	+4	+4

	0	1	2	3	4	5
+5	+5	+5	+5	+5	+5	+5

	0	1	2	3	4
+6	+6	+6	+6	+6	+6

	0	1	2	3
+7	+7	+7	+7	+7

	0	1	2
+8	+8	+8	+8

	0	1
+9	+9	+9

	0
+10	+10

Structurally Related Facts

Top Row	Adding 0
First Column	Adding to 0

Second Row	Adding 1
Second Column	Adding to 1

Third Row	Adding 2
Third Column	Adding to 2

The 10-Facts (boldface diagonal)

Doubles

Neighbors (consecutive numbers)

6 + 3, 3 + 6
5 + 3, 3 + 5

Basic Subtraction Facts

0	1	2	3	4	5	6	7	8	9	10
$0-0$	$1-0$	$2-0$	$3-0$	$4-0$	$5-0$	$6-0$	$7-0$	$8-0$	$9-0$	$10-0$
$1-1$	$2-1$	$3-1$	$4-1$	$5-1$	$6-1$	$7-1$	$8-1$	$9-1$	$10-1$	
$2-2$	$3-2$	$4-2$	$5-2$	$6-2$	$7-2$	$8-2$	$9-2$	$10-2$		
$3-3$	$4-3$	$5-3$	$6-3$	$7-3$	$8-3$	$9-3$	$10-3$			
$4-4$	$5-4$	$6-4$	$7-4$	$8-4$	$9-4$	$10-4$				
$5-5$	$6-5$	$7-5$	$8-5$	$9-5$	$10-5$					
$6-6$	$7-6$	$8-6$	$9-6$	$10-6$						
$7-7$	$8-7$	$9-7$	$10-7$							
$8-8$	$9-8$	$10-8$								
$9-9$	$10-9$									
$10-10$										

Structurally Related Facts

Top Row   Subtracting 0
First Column   Remainder of 0

Second Row   Subtracting 1
Second Column   Remainder of 1

Third Row   Subtracting 2
Third Column   Remainder of 2

Subtracting from 10 (boldface diagonal)

▨ Subtracting from Doubles

▨ Subtracting from Neighbors

☐ $9-3, 9-6$
   $8-3, 8-5$

Using the Lesson Plans

In the Structural Arithmetic Program children make their own discoveries in mathematics through experimenting with the materials. Writing in the workbook is only a small part of the program. The illustrations enable children to recall the special characteristics of each new concept. Teachers should read each lesson plan carefully before beginning instruction with the class.

Answer Key: A reduced version of the workbook page with answers indicated is conveniently located with each lesson plan.

Purpose: Each lesson contains a statement of the purpose of the experiments for that lesson.

Group Activity: The actual teaching is done *before* children open their workbooks. Children should work with the materials for several days (or even longer), until they thoroughly understand the concepts. The value of dynamic teaching lies in the teacher's use of his or her own statements and questions and the opportunities this provides for children to respond. Thus, this teacher's guide gives only a brief outline for each experiment. The experiments are illustrated and described in more detail in *Experimenting with Numbers.** The sequence in which they are presented corresponds to the developmental steps in children's learning. Suggestions are given for helping children who are having difficulty, and additional experiments are provided for this purpose.

Workbook Page: The workbook activities are the culmination of the children's work. Following each group of experiments, the students record the essential features of the experiments in their workbooks or on paper. The work on each page tests whether students have understood the lesson.

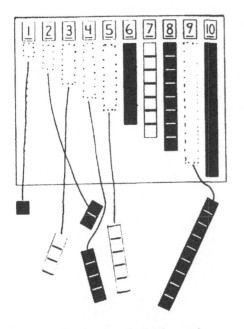

Purpose: To develop the basic number concepts that lie behind each number, or numeral; to learn the name of each number, how to count, and how to enumerate objects.

LESSON 1. The Counting Board: Matching Number Blocks with Numbers

Note: A numeral is a symbol, or configuration of lines, like a letter. Numerals are introduced on number markers, which the children fit into the counting board, thus learning that they are symbols that stand for a certain number of units. In general usage, however, symbols or numerals (1, 2, 3) are called numbers, for example, *telephone number, house number.* Structural Arithmetic therefore refers to numerical symbols as numbers rather than numerals.

Group Activity

Children learn to enumerate objects by counting the cubes in each groove of the counting board. They use this skill to discover the name of each block. As they remove the cubes that fill one groove, such as 3, they recite a counting word in time with each move: "1, 2, 3." Then they substitute the 3-block for the three cubes. At the same time they have discovered that the name of the block is "three." (*ExN,* p. 23, #1)*

Playing the Snake Game in the counting board is an exciting way for children to practice matching blocks with their corresponding numbers. Divide the group into two teams. The team members take turns picking a number from a pool of face-down number symbols, including zero. The child who picks the number symbol, names it, and puts the corresponding block in the counting board in the correct groove, can claim that block for the team's snake. The team that has the longer snake of blocks wins. (*ExN,* p. 45, #3)

Workbook Page

The children draw a line between each numbered groove and its corresponding number block.

* *ExN* refers to M. Stern, *Experimenting with Numbers* (Cambridge, Mass.: Educators Publishing Service, Inc.) 1988.

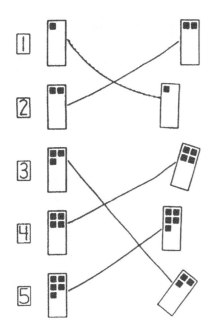

Purpose: To discover new characteristics for the numbers from 1 to 10 by working with patterns of cubes and the pattern boards.

LESSON 2. Matching Numbers and Like Patterns

Group Activity

The children learn to recognize and name each number pattern. Give each child an empty pattern board. On your display card, build different patterns with cubes. The child who has the corresponding pattern board names it, fills it with your cubes, and puts it in its proper place in the sequence from 1 to 10. Children learn the vocabulary *too few* and *too many* when they try to match the wrong pattern with their board. (*ExN*, p. 29, #1)

Play the Calling-Back Game to give children practice in matching number symbols with pattern boards. Give each child a pattern board. Keep the number markers in a pile. Hold up a number marker and ask, "Who has the pattern board that goes with this number?" The child who has the corresponding board claims the number marker, says its name, and puts that board in its place in the sequence. (*ExN*, p. 49, #1)

Workbook Page

The children draw a line from each numbered pattern to its matching pattern board. Patterns 1 to 5 are easy to recognize at a glance. Do not encourage counting. Go over the page orally first, if necessary.

Purpose: To discover the characteristics of odd and even numbers; to match the number patterns with their corresponding number symbols.

LESSON 3. The Characteristics of Odd and Even Numbers

Group Activity

Teach the even patterns by filling pattern boards 1 to 10 with cubes and arranging them in sequence. Point to the 2-pattern and say, "These 2 cubes are partners. We call this pattern even." Ask children to find other even pattern boards. You can ask them to dump the cubes out of certain boards by saying, "Dump out the biggest even number," and so forth. Do the same with the odd number boards. (*ExN*, p. 31, #5, #6)

Play the Sticker Game to give practice in matching symbols with patterns. Place the empty pattern boards in sequence from 1 to 10. When the children's eyes are closed, hide a sticker beneath a board. Say "Open." Show them a number symbol such as 9 and say, "This tells you where the sticker is hidden." Call on a child to locate it. Let the children take turns being teacher. (*ExN*, p. 49, #2)

Workbook Page

The children draw a line between each numbered space and the pattern board designated by that number.

A. Elicit that the pattern boards in place are the odd numbers; the children indicate where each even number pattern belongs, or "lives."
B. Elicit that the pattern boards in place are the even numbers; the children indicate where each odd number pattern belongs.

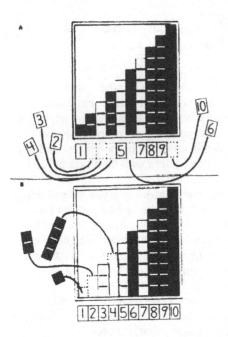

Purpose: To study the structure of the stair; to match the numbers 1 to 10 with the blocks in the stair.

LESSON 4. Matching Numbers with Number Blocks in the Stair

Group Activity

Scatter blocks 1 to 10 on the table and have the children build the stair in the 10-box. Start the sequence by placing blocks 1, 2, and 3 in the lower left corner of the box. This task may be difficult for some children. If so, align each block with the edge of the table; then ask the children to pick the smallest block each time and put it in the stair as the next step. (*ExN*, pp. 26 and 27)

Use the counting board filled with blocks to teach the positions represented by *before*, *after*, and *between*. These experiments can also be carried out with the blocks in the stair as it stands in the 10-box. (*ExN*, pp. 30 and 31, #9)

Workbook Page

A. The children draw a line from each scattered number marker to its place in the sequence from 1 to 10.

B. The children draw a line from each scattered block to its place in the stair.

LESSON 5. Learning to Write 1

Group Activity

Display the empty counting board, pattern board 1, the cubes, and the number markers. Ask a child to put a cube into the 1-board and state how many it holds. Have a child put the 1-cube in the first groove of the counting board and place number marker 1 above it.

Explain that some objects come "just one all alone." Show pictures of everyday things that come in ones. These might include the sun, the moon, a nose, a mouth, and so on. Elicit that *1* also stands for first place.

Writing *1:* Write a *1* on the chalkboard and have children name it. Draw a small arrow along the line and elicit that this indicates the direction in which the line is to be drawn. As the children draw *1*s in the air, check that they go from top to bottom. Write *1*s on the chalkboard and have children trace them.

Sensorimotor Exercises (for children who need more work)

Writing letters and numbers requires the ability to gauge the length of a line and to start and stop in time when writing this line. Children who have difficulty need special exercises such as the one in which they draw the rungs in a ladder. It helps when they dictate to themselves directions such as "start, stop." For more details, see *Drawing straight lines* on page 7.

Workbook Page

A. The children trace the *1*s and write *1*s in the empty boxes.

B. The children first tell you how many items are in each picture and then write the number under each picture.

C. The children trace each number *1* and then draw a picture of one simple object in each box.

Purpose: To learn to write the symbol *1* and to study the quantity for which it stands and the place it comes in the sequence.

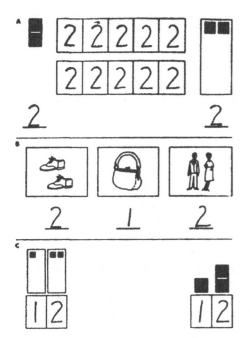

Purpose: To learn to write the symbol *2* and to study the quantity for which it stands and the place it comes in the sequence.

Group Activity

Display the empty counting board, the pattern boards, cubes, and number markers. Ask a child to put cubes into the 2-board and state how many it holds. Have a child put the 2-block in the second groove of the counting board and place number 2 above it.

Show pictures of everyday things that come in twos (or pairs), such as mittens and shoes. Elicit names of other things that come in twos, such as twins, two wheels of a bicycle, two eyes, and so on.

Writing *2:* Write a *2* on the chalkboard and have children name it. As children draw *2*s in the air, check that they go from top to bottom. Write *2*s on the chalkboard and have children trace them.

Sensorimotor Exercises (for children who need more work)

Help children draw a vertical string of loops on the chalkboard. When they can do this smoothly, have them break off after the first loop and form a *2*. Have them draw several *2*s and ask them to circle the best one. For more details, see *Drawing loops at the chalkboard* on page 7.

Workbook Page

A. The children trace the *2*s and write *2*s in the empty boxes.

B. The children first tell you how many items are in each picture and then write the number under each picture.

C. The children label the pattern boards and blocks studied so far.

Purpose: To learn to write the symbol *3* and to study the quantity for which it stands and the place it comes in the sequence.

LESSON 7. Learning to Write *3*

Group Activity

Display the empty counting board, the pattern boards, cubes, and number markers. Ask a child to put cubes into the 3-board and state how many it holds. Have a child put the 3-block in the third groove of the counting board and place number marker 3 above it.

Show pictures of everyday things that come in threes. These might include a tricycle, a triangle, triplets, a three-legged stool, or a clover leaf with three leaflets.

Place number markers 1, 2, and 3 face down. Ask each of three children to select a number marker and line up in sequence. The child with number 1 comes first, the child with number 2, second, and the child with number 3, third. Elicit that the child with number 3 is only one person. The number 3 tells in what *order* the person comes, in third place. Elicit that the child with number 2 is in *second* place and the child with 1, in *first* place. In this activity the children learn that numbers also indicate the order in which things come.

Writing *3:* Write a *3* on the chalkboard and have children name it. Have children draw *3*s in the air and trace *3*s on the chalkboard.

Sensorimotor Exercises (for children who need more work)

Help children make a vertical string of loops on the chalkboard. Have them break off after the first loop and form a *3*. For more details, see *Drawing loops at the chalkboard* on page 7.

Workbook Page

A. The children trace the *3*s and write *3*s in the empty boxes.

B. The children first tell you how many items are in each picture and then write the number under each picture.

C. The children label the pattern boards and blocks studied so far.

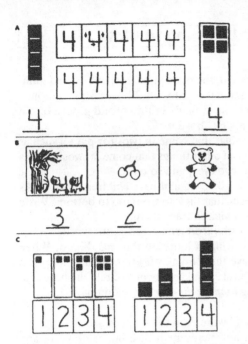

Purpose: To learn to write the symbol *4* and to study the quantity for which it stands and the place it comes in the sequence.

LESSON 8. Learning to Write 4

Group Activity

Display the empty counting board, the pattern boards, cubes, and number markers. Ask a child to put cubes into the 4-board and state how many it holds. Have a child put the 4-block and number marker 4 in place in the counting board.

Show pictures of everyday things that come in fours. These might include legs on a table or chair, legs or paws on an animal, corners of a square, and wheels on a car.

Place number markers 1 to 4 face down and choose four children to take one. Ask each to go to the table and get as many cubes as the number marker tells them to. Elicit that this time the numbers tell them how many items to get and not the order to take turns in.

Writing *4*: Write a *4* on the chalkboard and have children name it. Have children draw *4*s in the air and trace *4*s on the chalkboard.

Sensorimotor Exercises (for children who need more work)

Have the children do the straight line exercises described on page 7. Now have them write a *4*, saying to themselves, "Down, over, and way down." Have each child write several sets of numbers *1, 2, 3, 4*, keeping them uniform in size. Ask them to put a "frame" around the best set of numbers.

Workbook Page

A. The children trace the *4*s and write *4*s in the empty boxes.

B. The children first tell you how many items are in each picture and then write the number under each picture.

C. The children label the pattern boards and blocks studied so far.

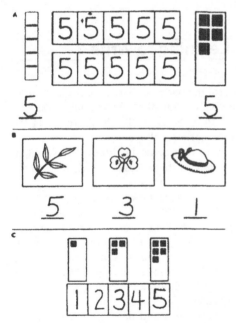

Purpose: To learn to write the symbol *5* and to study the quantity for which it stands and the place it comes in the sequence.

LESSON 9. Learning to Write 5

Group Activity

Display the empty counting board, the pattern boards, cubes, and number markers. Ask various children to put blocks 1 to 5 in the counting board and to label the *fifth* block with number marker 5. Have a child line up pattern boards 1 to 5 in sequence and fill the *fifth* board with cubes. Elicit that 5 is an odd number because it has an extra, odd, cube without a partner.

Show pictures of everyday things that come in fives. These might include fingers on a hand, toes on a foot, a five-pointed star, and a flower with five petals.

Have children hold up their right hands. Ask them to separate their fingers to make groups of 1 and 4, 2 and 3, 3 and 2, and 4 and 1. They can see these groups at a glance. This is to encourage them to work with structures and not to count fingers.

Writing *5*: Write a *5* on the chalkboard and have children name it. Have children draw *5*s in the air and trace *5*s on the chalkboard.

Sensorimotor Exercises (for children who need more work)

After mastering straight line exercises and loops, children have the skills to write *5*, but they may need a way to remember the order of the strokes. Saying these words can guide them, "Down, around, and give it a hat."

Workbook Page

A. The children trace the *5*s, starting at the heavy line each time. They write *5*s in the empty boxes.

B. Point out that each picture shows an odd number of items; the children label each picture.

C. Only the odd pattern boards are shown. The children write or trace the numbers you tell them to: "The biggest odd number (5), the smallest odd number (1), another odd number (3), the number that comes between 1 and 3 (2), and the number that comes before 5 (4)."

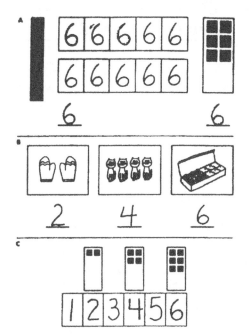

Purpose: To learn to write the symbol 6 and to study the quantity for which it stands and the place it comes in the sequence.

Group Activity

Display the empty counting board, the pattern boards, cubes, and number markers. Ask various children to put blocks 1 to 6 in the counting board and to label the *sixth* block with number marker 6. Have a child line up pattern boards 1 to 6 in sequence and fill the *sixth* board with cubes. Elicit that 6 is an even number. Each cube has a partner.

Show pictures of everyday things that come in sixes. These might include legs on an insect, a flower with six petals, a window with six panes, and a snowflake.

Writing 6: Write a 6 on the chalkboard and have children name it. Have children draw 6s in the air and trace 6s on the chalkboard. Remind them in which direction 6 goes.

Sensorimotor Exercises (for children who need more work)

Help children make a counterclockwise vertical string of loops at the chalkboard. Have them break off after the first loop to make a 6. For more details, see *Drawing loops at the chalkboard* on page 7.

Playing a writing game: Give each child a sheet of paper with a row of six boxes. Divide the children into two teams. A player throws two dice and selects one number from the choice of two numbers. All the members of that team write this number in its proper box in the row. The teams alternate throwing the dice. The team that fills all its boxes first wins.

Workbook Page

A. The children trace the 6s and write 6s in the empty boxes.

B. Elicit that each picture shows an even number of items; the children label each picture.

C. The children write or trace the numbers you tell them to: "The biggest even number (6), the smallest even number (2), another even number (4), the number that comes after 2 (3), the first number (1), and the number that comes between 4 and 6 (5)."

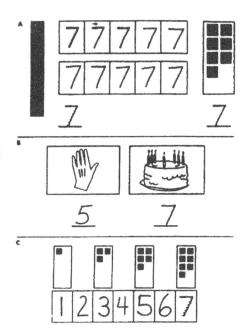

Purpose: To learn to write the symbol 7 and to study the quantity for which it stands and the place it comes in the sequence.

Group Activity

Display the empty counting board, the pattern boards, cubes, and number markers. Ask various children to put blocks 1 to 7 in the counting board and to label the *seventh* block with number marker 7. Have a child line up pattern boards 1 to 7 in sequence and fill the *seventh* board with cubes. Elicit that 7 is an odd number because it has an extra, odd, cube without a partner.

The usual instance of something that comes in sevens is the week.

Writing 7: Write a 7 on the chalkboard and have children name it. Have children draw 7s in the air and trace 7s on the chalkboard. Remind them which direction 7 goes (for example, toward the door).

Sensorimotor Exercises (for children who need more work)

Children should work on the exercise found in *Drawing straight lines at the chalkboard* on page 7. They should make several 7s, saying "Over, down," and then they should "frame" the best 7.

Workbook Page

A. The children trace the 7s and write 7s in the empty boxes.

B. Elicit that each picture shows an odd number of items; the children label each picture.

C. Only the odd pattern boards are shown. Ask the children to listen as you tell them which numbers to write: "The smallest odd number (1), the biggest odd number (7), the odd numbers that are left (3) and (5), the number between 5 and 7 (6), the number before 5 (4), and the number between 1 and 3 (2).

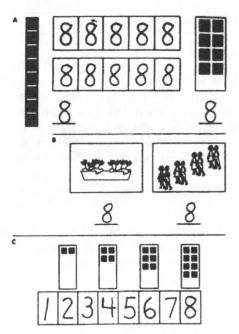

Purpose: To learn to write the symbol 8 and to study the quantity for which it stands and the place it comes in the sequence.

LESSON 12. Learning to Write 8

Group Activity

Display the empty counting board, the pattern boards, cubes, and number markers. Ask various children to put blocks 1 to 8 in the counting board and to label the *eighth* block with number marker 8. Have a child line up pattern boards 1 to 8 in sequence and fill the *eighth* board with cubes. Elicit that 8 is an even number. Each cube has a partner.

Show pictures of everyday things that come in eights. These might include an octagonal building, a stop sign, and an octopus.

Writing *8:* Write an *8* on the chalkboard and have children name it. The initial motion for making *8* is the letter *S*. As children draw *8*s in the air and trace *8*s on the chalkboard, have them say, "*S* and close it up." Have children write *8*s on the chalkboard and "frame" the best one.

Playing a writing game: Turn number markers 1 to 8 face down in a tray. Give each child a sheet of paper with a row of eight boxes. Divide the class into two teams. The children on each team take turns selecting a number marker, announcing it, and having their teammates write that number in its proper box on their papers. The winner is the team whose members fill all their boxes first.

Workbook Page

A. The children trace the *8*s and then write *8*s in the empty boxes.

B. Elicit that in one picture the total of 8 is grouped as two *4*s and in the other, as four pairs of 2. The children label each picture.

C. Elicit that this is a sequence of even pattern boards. Ask the children to listen as you tell them which numbers to write: "The biggest even number (8), the smallest even number (2), the other even numbers (4) and (6). Now write the number between 2 and 4 (3), between 4 and 6 (5), between 6 and 8 (7), and the first number (1)."

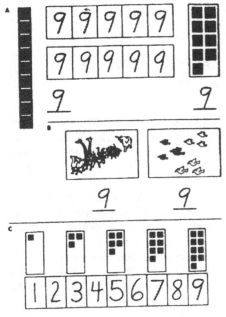

Purpose: To learn to write the symbol 9 and to study the quantity for which it stands and the place it comes in the sequence.

LESSON 13. Learning to Write 9

Group Activity

Display the counting board, the pattern boards, cubes, and number markers. Ask various children to put blocks 1 to 9 in the counting board and to label the *ninth* block with number marker 9. Have a child line up the pattern boards 1 to 9 in sequence and fill the *ninth* board with cubes. Explain that 9 is the biggest odd number they will study in this book.

Writing *9:* Write a *9* on the chalkboard and have children name it. Have children draw *9*s in the air and trace *9*s on the chalkboard.

Sensorimotor Exercises (for children who need more work)

Help children make a counterclockwise string of loops. Have them break off after the first loop and write a 9 by adding a stick to the loop. Have them say, "Around, up, and then down." See *Drawing loops at the chalkboard* on page 7.

Playing a writing game: Give each child a sheet of paper with a row of nine boxes. The children will write a number in each box. Divide the class into two teams. Give each team a scarf and hide a set of blocks from 1 to 9 under each scarf. Let each team build its own stair and at the same time write in the correct box the number of the block they have withdrawn from under their scarf. (The blocks may be selected in random order.) The winning team is the one that finishes first.

Workbook Page

A. The children trace the *9*s and then write *9*s in the empty boxes.

B. Elicit that each picture shows a different grouping of 9—four 2s and an extra elephant and three sets of 3 birds. The children label each picture.

C. Elicit that this is a sequence of odd pattern boards. Ask the children to write the sequence by tracing the odd numbers and then to write the missing even numbers.

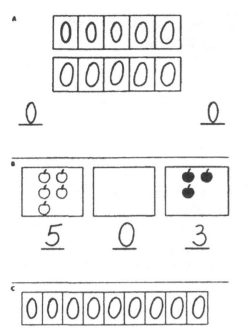

Purpose: To learn to write the symbol *0* and to learn that *0* stands for *nothing*—also called zero. In the block games it means "no blocks" or "no cubes."

LESSON 14. Learning to Write *0*

Group Activity
Use the number markers 1 to 9 and 0. Explain to the children that they are to get as many cubes as their number marker tells them to. Show them that 0 means they get no cubes at all. Then turn the number markers 1 to 9 and 0 face down and have the children take turns drawing a number and getting cubes. If the child who gets the marker with zero is devastated, give him or her another turn. The concept will have been made clear at that point.

Writing *0*: Write a *0* on the chalkboard and have children name it. Emphasize that they start at the top and move to the left. Have children draw *0*s in the air and trace *0*s on the chalkboard.

Sensorimotor Exercises (for children who need more work)
The exercises on drawing circles on page 7 give more ideas for helping children who have difficulty writing *0*.

Workbook Page
A. The children trace the *0*s, starting at the heavy line each time, and then write *0*s in the empty boxes.

B. The empty box is contrasted with boxes that contain apples. The children write the correct number under each box.

C. The children simply trace or write *0* in each box.

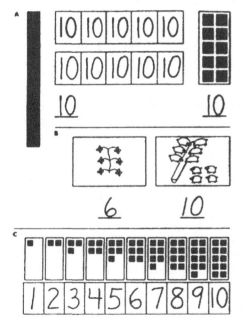

Purpose: To learn to write the symbol *10* and to study the quantity for which it stands and the place it comes in the sequence.

LESSON 15. Learning to Write *10*

Note: In teaching 10, do not discuss the use of 0 as a place holder. This concept is presented in *Structural Arithmetic II*.

Group Activity
Display the empty counting board, the pattern boards, cubes, and number markers. Ask various children to put blocks 1 to 10 in the counting board and to label the *tenth* block with number marker 10. Have a child line up pattern boards 1 to 10 in sequence and fill the *tenth* board with cubes. This is the biggest number the children will study in *Structural Arithmetic I*.

Show pictures of everyday things that come in tens. These might include fingers on both hands, toes on both feet, and pennies in a dime.

Playing the Snake Game: This is an excellent way to check children's knowledge of the numbers and corresponding blocks. Display the counting board with the blocks and number guide in place. Divide the children into two teams. Turn number markers 1 to 10 and 0 face down on a tray. The team members take turns selecting a number marker, placing it in the counting board, and withdrawing the corresponding block. They put this block on their team's snake of blocks. The team with the longest snake of blocks wins. If the child who gets the marker with zero is disappointed, give him or her another turn. (*ExN*, p. 45, #3)

Writing *10*: Write a *10* on the chalkboard and have children name it. Have children draw *10*s in the air and trace *10*s on the chalkboard.

Workbook Page
A. The children trace the *10*s and then write *10*s in the empty boxes.

B. Elicit that one picture shows 6 flowers and the other, a group of 6 pigs and a group of 4 pigs, which totals 10 pigs. The children label each picture.

C. The children see all the pattern boards, but only the even ones are labeled. Ask the children to write or trace all the numbers in succession.

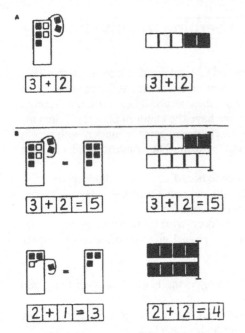

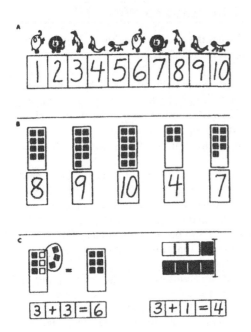

Purpose: To demonstrate with the Structural Arithmetic materials the action the plus sign stands for and the meaning of the equal sign. (Forming equations using the number markers enables children to read and record facts before they are secure in writing numbers.)

Purpose: To test ability to write the numbers *1* to *10*; to test ability to write a simple equation.

LESSON 16. Learning to Read and Write Equations

Group Activity

Display the counting board with the blocks and the number guide in place. When the children's eyes are closed, hide two blocks under a box. On top of the box place the number markers that stand for the blocks, for example, 3 + 2. Elicit that this says "three and two" or "three plus two." Lift the box and reveal the blocks. Introduce the equal sign after the plus sign has been mastered. Continue the game, hiding other blocks and recording them with symbols. Have the children show you which blocks they think you have hidden under the box. (*ExN*, p. 47, #7, #8)

Note: When the word *plus* is used, the verb is singular: 2 plus 2 *is* 4 (equals 4). However, the word *and* denotes plurality: 2 and 2 *are* 4 (equal 4).

Playing the Sticker Game: Place the empty pattern boards in sequence from 1 to 10. Tell the children to close their eyes while you hide a sticker beneath a board. Have the children open their eyes. Indicate with the number markers the position of the sticker: 6 + 1. A child reads, "Six plus one" and looks under pattern board 7 to claim the sticker. (*ExN*, p. 49, #2)

Workbook Page

A. Explain that the plus sign means "adding together two amounts." The children record the addends shown and join them by tracing the plus sign.

B. Explain that the equal sign means that something is "just as big as" the two amounts being added together. Tell the children that the equal sign is composed of two lines "just as big as each other." Go over the equations first; then the children complete them independently.

LESSON 17. Test: Writing Numbers and Equations

Group Activity

Give each child a strip of paper with 10 boxes on it like the one at the top of Lesson 17. Display the counting board and place the number markers next to it. Select a number marker, announce its name, and then place it in the proper space in the counting board. Each child writes that number in the correct box on her or his paper. The order in which to ask for numbers should be: the last numbers, the first numbers, and then the center numbers, 6, 7, and 8. For fun, let the children take the role of teacher and present the numbers to be written by their classmates.

Workbook Page

A. The children write the numbers *1* to *10*.

B. The children label each pattern with a number.

C. The children finish the equations independently.

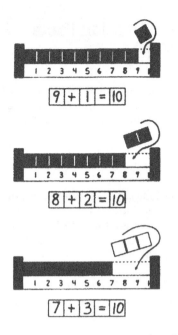

$9 + 1 = 10$

$8 + 2 = 10$

$7 + 3 = 10$

Purpose: To learn to write the addition facts discovered in the 10-box.

| 9 | 8 | 7 | | 10 |

$9 + 1 = 10$ $3 + 7 = 10$

$8 + 2 = 10$ $2 + 8 = 10$

$7 + 3 = 10$ $1 + 9 = 10$

Purpose: To find the missing addend when one addend and the sum are given.

LESSON 18. Addition Facts That Make 10

Group Activity

Play many games using the 10-box before carrying out the following demonstration. Take the 10-box and empty the blocks onto the table. Put a combination of blocks in the box, perhaps the 7- and 3-blocks. Say, "7 needs 3 to be as big as 10," as you measure the blocks with the 10-block. Ask a child to put two other blocks in the box that together make 10 and to "tell the story." Encourage the children to use their own words; if they do, it shows that they understand what they are doing. (*ExN*, p. 38, #7)

Teach the children how to record an addition fact from the 10-box. Set out the number markers, including the signs for plus and equals. Step by step the children record each move with the number markers. Then they read back their newly formed equation: 7 plus 3 equals 10. (*ExN*, p. 56, #1)

Workbook Page

Elicit that each pair of blocks measures (or equals) 10. Go over the combinations orally first; then children complete the equations by writing the numbers in the boxes.

LESSON 19. Finding Missing Addends in the 10-Box

Note: When the combinations of blocks are placed in the 10-box in sequence, the children can use this organization to reason that if 9 needs 1 to make 10, then 8 needs 2, and 7 needs 3 to make 10.

Group Activity

Play the Hiding Game, in which the missing addend must be named. Display the filled 10-box. Have the children close their eyes. Behind your back hide blocks for a combination that makes 10, putting one block in each hand. Say, "Open your eyes. I have 10 altogether. In one hand I have 8" (place it in the box). "What is in the other hand?" When a child answers, reveal the hidden block, and have the child put it in place in the 10-box. A child should state the fact: 8 plus 2 equals 10. (*ExN*, p. 39, #9)

Have the children build in the 10-box a vertical stair of blocks from 1 to 10. Turn the box around and have them build a vertical stair from 1 to 9. It will go in the opposite direction. Help the children mesh the two stairs together as they recite the 10-facts: "1 needs 9, 2 needs 8 . . . 10 needs no other block." (*ExN*, p. 36, #3)

Workbook Page

This illustration can be understood only after children have worked with the materials. Elicit the names of the pairs of blocks that make 10. Point to the equation that records the first pair. Have a child read, "9 and what equal (or make) 10?" The children write the missing addend in the empty space in the equation. They complete the page independently.

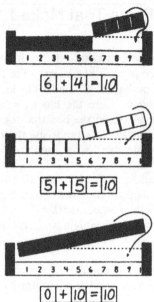

$6 + 4 = 10$

$5 + 5 = 10$

$0 + 10 = 10$

Purpose: To learn to write addition facts discovered in the 10-box, including the zero fact.

LESSON 20. Writing More Addition Facts with Sums of 10

Group Activity

Empty the blocks from the 10-box and give the small blocks to the children. Put a big block, such as 9, into the 10-box. Ask, "Who has the block that fits with 9?" Have children name both blocks together, 9 and 1. Put the 10-block into the box and ask if another block can fit with it. Have children state this as "10 and no other block" before they learn to say, "10 and zero." In this way you will know they understand the concept behind the word *zero*. (*ExN*, p. 35, #2)

The Scarf Game provides an oral check of the children's knowledge of the combinations that make 10. Hide all the blocks from the 10-box beneath a scarf. Hold up the 10-box. Say, "Ask me for two blocks that make 10." Give the children the blocks they request so they can place them in the 10-box by themselves. (*ExN*, p. 38, #8)

Workbook Page

Elicit that the blocks in each picture measure 10. Go over the combinations orally first. Make certain that children know how to write an equation. They complete the page independently.

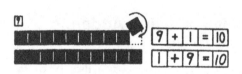

$9 + 1 = 10$
$1 + 9 = 10$

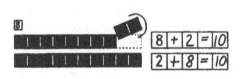

$8 + 2 = 10$
$2 + 8 = 10$

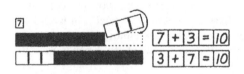

$7 + 3 = 10$
$3 + 7 = 10$

Purpose: To discover the commutative property of addition—that changing the order of the addends does not change the sum.

LESSON 21. The Commutative Property of Addition

Note: Although the children do not use the term *commutative property*, they show that they understand it by changing the order of the blocks in the pair.

Group Activity

Scatter the blocks from the 10-box on the table. Ask a child to get two blocks that make 10, put them in the 10-box, and recite the fact, perhaps 8 plus 2 equals 10. Now ask the children to find the twin set of blocks. Ask them to make a different fact with the same blocks: $2 + 8 = 10$. (*ExN*, p. 36, #4)

The next experiment allows the children an overall view of all ten 10-facts. Have children build a stair in the 10-box and then complete each row to make 10. When the children's eyes are closed, hide one pair of blocks, perhaps 9 and 1. When they open their eyes, ask them to state which pair is missing. Encourage them to find the twin pair still in the box, but in the reverse order (1 and 9). (Of course, $5 + 5$ and the 10-block have no twins.) (*ExN*, p. 37, #5)

Workbook Page

Help children finish the pairs of equations, which demonstrate the commutative property of addition.

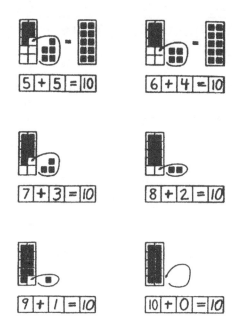

$$5 + 5 = 10$$ $$6 + 4 = 10$$

$$7 + 3 = 10$$ $$8 + 2 = 10$$

$$9 + 1 = 10$$ $$10 + 0 = 10$$

Purpose: To study the combinations that make 10 by knowing the subgroups, or number patterns, that make up the 10-pattern.

LESSON 22. Addition Facts That Make 10: Using the Pattern Boards

Note: When you introduce the patterns with cubes, build them on display cards. The crisscross grill of lines forms ten spaces to help children build the patterns with cubes. These spaces enable children to see that the 9-pattern needs 1 cube to fill the whole card, or make 10 (9 + 1 = 10). The 8-pattern needs 2 cubes (8 + 2 = 10), and the 7-pattern needs 3 cubes to make 10 (7 + 3 = 10). (*ExN*, p. 15, #7, #8)

Group Activity

Give each child an empty pattern board. Build patterns with cubes 1 to 10 on your display card and have each child claim the one that will fill his or her pattern board.

Next, ask the child who has pattern board 9 to transfer the cubes to your display card. Ask, "What does 9 need to make 10?" The child with the 1-pattern gives you the 1-cube to add to the 9-pattern and recites, "9 needs 1 to make 10." Do the same with the 8-pattern, the 7-pattern, and the 6-pattern. Leave the display card empty and ask, "What does 0 need to make 10?" The child who has pattern board 10 gives you the cubes for the display card and recites, "0 needs 10 to make 10." Build the 5-pattern on the display card and ask, "What does 5 need to make 10?" The child with pattern board 5 gives you the cubes for the display card and recites that fact. (New Game)

Workbook Page

The children write each equation beneath the pattern boards. Go over the page to be sure they recognize each pattern and do not need to count the cubes.

$$6 + 4 = 10$$ $$4 + 6 = 10$$

$$8 + 2 = 10$$ $$2 + 8 = 10$$

$$10 + 0 = 10$$ $$0 + 10 = 10$$

Purpose: To study the even combinations that make 10 by recognizing the even number patterns that make the 10-pattern.

LESSON 23. Adding Even Numbers to Make 10: Introducing the Column Form of Addition

Group Activity

Review the concept of even numbers. Arrange all the pattern boards in sequence from 1 to 10. Ask a child to move the first even board down and name it (2). The children take turns moving all the other even boards down and naming them. Ask children to remove the odd boards. Fill the even boards with cubes. Now have children select pairs of boards whose patterns of cubes when added together equal 10. (The 10-board alone; the 8-board and 2-board; the 6- and 4-boards). (*ExN*, p. 31, #5)

Give each child a display card and elicit that it can hold 10 cubes. Ask children to build an even number on their display cards. On your display card, build a pattern (such as 6), using cubes of one color. Ask how many more cubes 6 needs to fill the card, or to make 10. Give it to the child who has 4 cubes and elicit that 6 needs 4 to make 10. Build different even patterns that need another even addend to make 10. Elicit that two even numbers make an even number. Discourage counting. (New Game)

Workbook Page

Explain that in the column form of addition the equal sign is replaced by a horizontal line drawn beneath the numbers to be added.

A. Elicit that 6 + 4 makes 10. Point out that 4 + 6 = 10 is called the reverse fact.

B. Elicit that an even pattern needs an even pattern to make an even pattern.

C. Explain that 10 cats already fill the board; no more can come. However, the empty board will need 10 cats to come in and fill it.

Purpose: To study the odd combinations that make 10 by recognizing the odd number patterns that make the 10-pattern.

LESSON 24. Adding Odd Numbers to Make 10

Group Activity
Review the concept of odd numbers by arranging all the pattern boards filled with cubes in sequence from 1 to 10. Describe an odd number—explain that the top pair of cubes are partners, and the last cube is all alone. Ask children to find patterns with one cube all alone (1, 3, 5, 7, 9).

Have children remove the even patterns. Set a display card before the children. Select an odd pattern board (perhaps 7), remove the cubes from the board, and put them on the display card. Ask which other pattern board could be added to 7 to make 10. Elicit that two odd numbers make the even number 10. The story is $7 + 3 = 10$. Do also $9 + 1 = 10$ and $5 + 5 = 10$. (*ExN*, p. 31, #6)

Workbook Page
A. Elicit that 9 needs 1 to make 10. Make sure children realize that $1 + 9$ is the reverse fact.
B. Elicit that 7 needs 3 to make 10; $3 + 7$ is the reverse fact.
C. The double, $5 + 5$, is shown twice—the second time as a story to tell in words. Encourage children to tell this addition story and then record it. There is no reverse fact for a double.

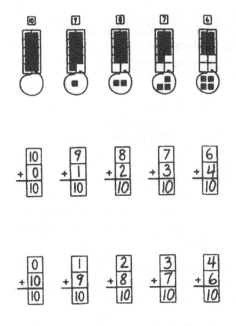

Purpose: To study the combinations that make 10 by adding number patterns; to figure out and record each reverse fact.

LESSON 25. Addition Facts with Sums of 10

Group Activity
For some children it is easier to visualize the number patterns than the number blocks. Place on a paper mat in front of each child a small number of cubes, either 1, 2, 3, 4, 5, or no cubes. Fill pattern boards 5 to 10 with cubes, and arrange them in order, covered by a scarf. Call on a child to name his or her pattern of cubes, perhaps "four," and then to ask you for the hidden board that needs these 4 cubes to make 10: "Please give me the 6-board." The child then keeps the 6-board, placing the 4 cubes on the empty section of the board to make 10 in all and recites the story, "6 needs 4 to make 10." The child with no cubes asks for the 10-board. This game helps children visualize these combinations. (New Game)

Workbook Page
Explain that the pattern card below each number demonstrates an addition fact with the sum of 10. Children complete the examples beneath the pattern cards. Then they figure out the reverse facts and write them at the bottom of the page. The first set is already done: $10 + 0 = 10$; $0 + 10 = 10$. Draw attention to the illustration of pattern cards and point out that as the "top" addend gets smaller, the other addend must get bigger so that together they always equal 10.

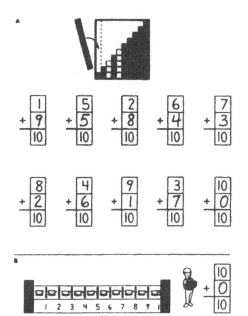

$$\begin{array}{r}1\\+9\\\hline 10\end{array}\quad\begin{array}{r}5\\+5\\\hline 10\end{array}\quad\begin{array}{r}2\\+8\\\hline 10\end{array}\quad\begin{array}{r}6\\+4\\\hline 10\end{array}\quad\begin{array}{r}7\\+3\\\hline 10\end{array}$$

$$\begin{array}{r}8\\+2\\\hline 10\end{array}\quad\begin{array}{r}4\\+6\\\hline 10\end{array}\quad\begin{array}{r}9\\+1\\\hline 10\end{array}\quad\begin{array}{r}3\\+7\\\hline 10\end{array}\quad\begin{array}{r}10\\+0\\\hline 10\end{array}$$

|⚬|⚬|⚬|⚬|⚬|⚬|⚬|⚬|⚬|⚬|
1 2 3 4 5 6 7 8 9

$$\begin{array}{r}10\\+0\\\hline 10\end{array}$$

Purpose: To test knowledge of the 10-facts in column form with one addend missing.

LESSON 26. Test: Addition Facts with Sums of 10—Missing Addends, Column Form

Group Activity
Play the Hiding Game with the blocks from the 10-box. Display the filled 10-box. Have the children close their eyes. Behind your back hide blocks for a combination that makes 10, putting one block in each hand. Say, "Open your eyes. I have 10 altogether. In one hand I have 8 (place it in the box). What is in the other hand?" When the child answers, reveal the hidden block (the missing addend), and have a child put it in place in the box. The child should state the fact: 8 plus 2 equals 10. This child should then play the role of teacher, or leader. When the children's eyes are shut, the leader must measure the two blocks in the 10-box to be sure they make 10; then continue with the game. (*ExN*, p. 39, #9 and p. 9, #7)

Workbook Page
A. Explain that this is a test of the 10-facts. Point to the picture at the top and elicit that the picture should remind them where they learned these facts.

B. Go over the problem in the picture orally first by having several children tell the story in their own words. If necessary, explain that the boy is holding an empty tray.

$$9+1=10 \qquad 2+8=10$$
$$10+0=10 \qquad 4+6=10$$
$$3+7=10 \qquad 1+9=10$$
$$5+5=10 \qquad 6+4=10$$
$$7+3=10 \qquad 8+2=10$$

|🐱|🐱|🐱|🐱|🐱|🐱|🐱|🐱| |
1 2 3 4 5 6 7 8 9

$$\begin{array}{r}8\\+2\\\hline 10\end{array}$$

$$8+2=10$$

Purpose: To test knowledge of the 10-facts in equation form with one addend missing.

LESSON 27. Test: Addition Facts with Sums of 10—Missing Addends, Equation Form

Group Activity
Review the written 10-facts with a card game. Write on ten cards the equations in Lesson 27. Place the number markers 1 to 9 and 0 face up on a tray. Place the number blocks nearby. Have a child turn up a card, read it, demonstrate the equation with the blocks, and put the correct number marker in the equation as the missing addend. (*ExN*, p. 56, #2)

Demonstrate word problems by using number blocks to represent the amounts in your story. Say, "I had 8 bananas. I bought 2 more." Have a child place these blocks end to end. Ask, "How many did I have?" The child answers, "10." Children may also record the story with number markers: $8+2=10$. (*ExN*, p. 59, #7)

Workbook Page
A. Children write the missing addend in each equation.

B. A child discusses the story problem orally first. Then children complete the page.

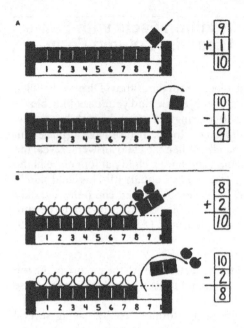

Purpose: To discover the relationship between subtraction and addition; to learn the meaning of the minus sign.

LESSON 28. The Relationship between Addition and Subtraction

Note: The relationship between addition and subtraction is one of doing and undoing, like wrapping a parcel and unwrapping it. The plus sign stands for putting two blocks together; now the minus sign stands for diminishing the total by taking one of the blocks away. The child will say, "10 *minus* 1," "10 *take away* 1," or "10 *less* 1." When acting out an addition story, children understand there will be more in the end. When acting out a subtraction story, they will see that there is less in the end. The following experiments dramatize the opposite character of addition and subtraction.

Group Activity

Place the blocks and number markers on the table. Tell an addition story such as, "I had 9 apples and bought 1 more." Have a child place the corresponding blocks end to end to dramatize this story, and then state, "9 plus 1 equals 10." Now cover the blocks with a box and tell this related subtraction story, "I had 10 apples and I ate 1." Demonstrate this by withdrawing the 1-cube from under the box. Have the children use the number markers to record what you said and did: $10 - 1 = 9$. They will conclude that the 9-block is still under the box. Tell them that 9 is called the remainder because it "remains" under the box. They should lift up the box and check the remainder. (*ExN*, p. 58, #6)

Workbook Page

A. Elicit that in the top illustration the 1-block is added to the 9-block. In the companion picture children see the "undoing" of this addition: the 1-block is subtracted from 10.

B. The children tell you the story for adding apples and then the opposite story in which 2 apples are subtracted from 10 apples. They complete the examples by themselves.

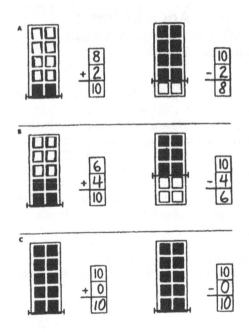

Purpose: To learn the opposite nature of the actions that the plus and minus signs stand for—addition means becoming *more;* subtraction means becoming *less.*

LESSON 29. Addition Facts That Make 10 and the Related Subtraction Facts

Group Activity

It is important to start with experiments that give children practice in understanding that subtraction is the reverse of addition. Arrange the even pattern boards in sequence: 2, 4, 6, 8, 10. Give each child a display card and 10 cubes.

Start with addition. Build the 2-pattern on your display card and have the children do the same on their cards. Add 2 cubes to your pattern and have them do the same to their patterns. Ask them what they did ("I added 2 cubes: 2 plus 2 is 4"). Continue up to $8 + 2 = 10$. Now subtract 2 cubes from your 10-pattern. They do the same with their patterns. Have them tell you what they did ("I took away 2 cubes: 10 minus 2 is 8"). Work down to $2 - 2 = 0$. (*ExN*, p. 32, #7, #8)

Build an even pattern with cubes on your display card. Move it behind a screen. Either add enough cubes to make 10, or take a few away. When you show the changed pattern, ask children what you did. They record your action with the number markers, using either the plus or the minus sign. (*ExN*, p. 54, #12)

Workbook Page

Each set of examples has an addition fact and a related subtraction fact. Elicit that the plus sign stands for adding some cubes to a pattern; the minus sign records that these cubes are subtracted from the 10-pattern. Go over the examples orally. The children complete the page independently.

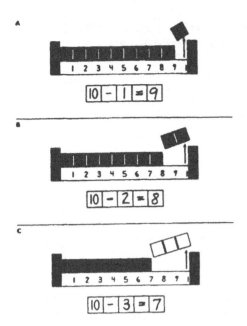

Purpose: To study the subtraction facts in the 10-box.

LESSON 30. Subtracting from 10

Group Activity

Review the 10-facts. Arrange the combinations of blocks in the 10-box in sequence, starting with 1 + 9. Cover these combinations that make 10 with a notebook. Reveal the first combination by drawing back the notebook. The children say, "1 and 9 make 10." Ask them to figure out the next combination and say what they think it is ("2 and 8 are 10"). Reveal it. Continue in the same way until all the combinations have been reviewed orally. (*ExN*, p. 37, #6)

The Scarf Game gives excellent practice in oral subtraction. Children close their eyes and you hide a combination of two blocks from the 10-box under a scarf. Say, "Open your eyes. I hid two blocks that make 10. If Ann takes 6 away, what will be left?" Help Ann remove the 6-block. The child called on says, "The 4-block remains." Let the children look under the scarf. They should state the full equation: "10 take away 6 leaves 4." (*ExN*, p. 58, #5)

Workbook Page

In each illustration the children see two blocks that together make 10. Explain that the minus sign indicates that the total 10 will be diminished. In A the 1-block has been removed and the remainder is 9. The children say *minus* or *take away* when reading the equation.

The children complete the equations independently.

LESSON 31. Subtracting from 10

Group Activity

Review the combinations that make 10 by playing Which Blocks Are Missing? In the 10-box arrange all the combinations in order from 1 + 9 to 10 + 0. While the children's eyes are closed, remove one pair of blocks. After the children open their eyes, call on someone to figure out which blocks are missing. Have the child return the missing combination. (*ExN*, p. 37, #5)

Carry out a subtraction example with the blocks. Place the combination of blocks 9 and 1 beneath a box. Tell a story such as "I had 10 puppies. I sold 9 of them." Remove the 9-block from under the box. Ask the children how many are left. The children should know that 1 cube is left. Have them record your story with number markers: $10 - 9 = 1$. (*ExN*, p. 58, #6)

Workbook Page

A. Elicit that the illustration $(10 - 9)$ is the reverse of the fact shown in *A* on page 30 $(10 - 1)$.

B. Elicit that $10 - 5 = 5$ has no reverse fact.

C. Elicit that since the whole 10-block is subtracted from 10, "nothing," or no block, remains. This remainder will be recorded by 0.

The children complete the equations independently.

Purpose: To review the combinations that make 10 and to use this knowledge to solve subtraction equations.

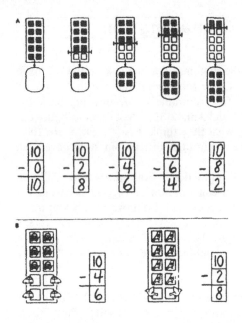

Purpose: To use the structure of the pattern board to learn about the subtraction of even numbers from 10.

LESSON 32. Subtracting Even Numbers from 10; Word Problems

Group Activity

Play the Screen Game by subtracting even numbers from the 10-pattern. Display pattern board 10 filled with cubes. Behind the screen subtract, for example, 6 cubes. Show the board again and ask what you did. The children should say that you took 6 cubes away from 10, and 4 remain. (*ExN*, p. 54, #11)

The children should invent word problems and tell subtraction stories. For this dramatic activity, give each child a display card and 10 cubes. Ask the children to invent and demonstrate problems in which they subtract even numbers from 10. "I had 10 kittens and I gave 6 away. How many are left for myself?" Since it is often impossible for children to ask a question when they can see the answer, have them cover the display card with a box. Then it is easy for them to ask, "How many are left?" (*ExN*, p. 53, #9)

Workbook Page

A. Point to the first example. It is obvious that if no cubes are subtracted from the 10-pattern, the 10 cubes remain unchanged ($10 - 0 = 10$). Children record this and the other facts. Check the reading of facts.

B. Go over the wording of each pictured problem, encouraging the children to tell the stories using their own words. They independently record the stories with numbers.

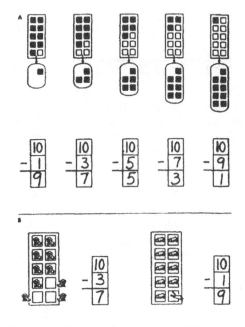

Purpose: To use the structure of the number patterns to learn about the subtraction of odd numbers from 10.

LESSON 33. Subtracting Odd Numbers from 10; Word Problems

Group Activity

Children need practice listening to word problems and comprehending the action; this will help them solve printed word problems later. Give each child a different pattern board filled with cubes. Tell a story beginning with the number pattern that one of the children has: "I have 10 books; I took 5 to school. How many were left at home?" Ask, "With which pattern can you show that story?" Have the child with the 10-pattern demonstrate the story by subtracting 5 cubes. Tell other number stories for other pattern boards. (*ExN*, p. 53, #10)

Give each child a pattern board with cubes. Now say, "Calling for the 9-board." When you have it ask, "Who has the pattern that 9 needs to make 10?" Collect the 1-cube and place it on the 9-board. Elicit that 9 plus 1 equals 10. Do the same for each combination. Next, play the Scarf Game. While the children's eyes are closed, hide a pattern board with a combination that makes 10 beneath a scarf. Say, "Open. I have 10 under here. If I subtract 1 cube (do so), what remains?" A child answers that 9 remains. You remove the scarf and reveal the 9-pattern. Do the same for all odd combinations that make 10. (*ExN*, p. 58, #5)

Workbook Page

A. Review the subtraction of odd numbers from 10. The children complete the examples.

B. Go over the pictured problem about dogs orally. The children should describe the situation with the frogs in their own words. They complete the examples independently.

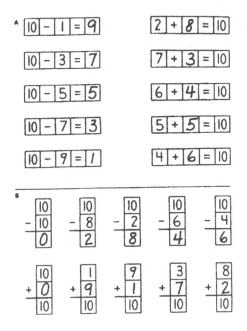

Purpose: To test subtracting from 10 and the addition facts with sums of 10.

LESSON 34. Test: Addition Facts That Make 10; Related Subtraction Facts

Group Activity

Play the Hiding Game in the 10-box as a quick review of the missing addend in addition. Scatter the blocks on the table. Have the children close their eyes. Behind your back hide blocks for a combination that makes 10, putting one block in each hand. Say, "Open your eyes. I have 10 altogether. In one hand I have 8. What is in the other hand?" Let the children take turns being leader in this game. When the children's eyes are shut, the leader must measure the two blocks in the 10-box to be sure they make 10; then she or he may continue with the game. (*ExN*, p. 39, #9)

Play the Scarf Game to review subtracting from 10. Children close their eyes and you hide a combination of two blocks from the 10-box under a scarf. Say, "Open your eyes. I hid two blocks that make 10. If Ann takes 6 away, what will be left?" Help Ann remove the 6-block. The child called on says, "The 4-block remains," looks under the scarf, gets the 4-block, and puts it with the 6-block to make 10. (*ExN*, p. 58, #5)

Workbook Page

A. Elicit that the left column contains subtraction equations, whereas the right column contains addition equations with missing addends.

B. Elicit that the top row contains subtraction examples; the bottom row, addition.

Children take the test independently. Those who have not mastered these facts should play more of the games suggested in Lessons 18 to 33 before taking this test again and the test for Lesson 35.

LESSON 35. Test: Addition Facts That Make 10; Related Subtraction Facts; Problem Solving with Oral Arithmetic

Group Activity

Review simple math vocabulary and the combinations that make 10 by playing a variation of the Scarf Game. Hide the blocks from the 10-box beneath a scarf. Give the children turns getting the blocks you ask for (they may peek under the scarf): "Get two blocks that added together make 10." Use other vocabulary: "Get two blocks with a sum of 10." Ask, "How much will you have if you get 5 and then add 5 more to it?" Have children write the equations on the chalkboard. (*ExN*, p. 38, #8)

Review the acting out of word problems in subtraction. Give each child a display card and 10 cubes. Have the children build the 10-pattern on their cards. Now tell a story in which some amount is subtracted from 10: "My class has 10 children. If 6 children go to gym, how many are left?" All the children demonstrate this story with cubes. Have a child recite the fact, $10 - 6 = 4$, and have another child write the fact on the chalkboard. (*ExN*, p. 53, #10)

Workbook Page

A. Elicit that this part of the test contains pairs of addition and subtraction equations.

B. Dictate these five examples for children to write in the spaces provided:

1. What is the sum of 9 and 1?
2. What do you get when you add 8 and 2?
3. If you have 5 in one hand and 5 in the other, how many do you have altogether?
4. If you have 10 marbles and lose 1, how many are left?
5. If you have 10 grapes and eat all 10, how many are left?

C. The children record the problem independently.

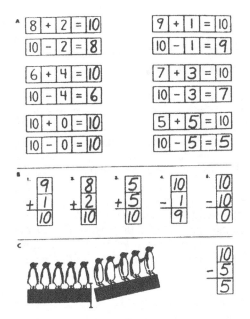

Purpose: To test the mastery of addition facts with sums of 10 and the related subtraction facts; to demonstrate the ability to record oral arithmetic examples.

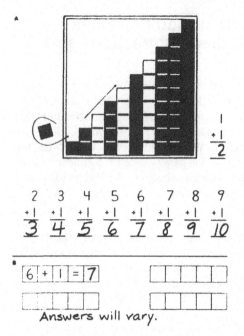

$$\begin{array}{r} 1 \\ +1 \\ \hline 2 \end{array}$$

$$\begin{array}{r} 2 \\ +1 \\ \hline 3 \end{array} \quad \begin{array}{r} 3 \\ +1 \\ \hline 4 \end{array} \quad \begin{array}{r} 4 \\ +1 \\ \hline 5 \end{array} \quad \begin{array}{r} 5 \\ +1 \\ \hline 6 \end{array} \quad \begin{array}{r} 6 \\ +1 \\ \hline 7 \end{array} \quad \begin{array}{r} 7 \\ +1 \\ \hline 8 \end{array} \quad \begin{array}{r} 8 \\ +1 \\ \hline 9 \end{array} \quad \begin{array}{r} 9 \\ +1 \\ \hline 10 \end{array}$$

$6 + 1 = 7$ ☐☐☐☐☐

☐☐☐☐☐ ☐☐☐☐☐

Answers will vary.

Purpose: To discover that adding 1 to a number results in reaching the next highest number, or the neighbor.

LESSON 36. Adding 1 to a Number; The Climbing 1

Group Activity
Have the children build the stair in the 10-box. Place an extra 1-block on the first step of the stair and state that 1 and 1 equal 2. Have the children move the 1-block up the steps, reciting the fact each time until they reach, "9 and 1 are 10." Use the word *neighbor* to mean the next number. (*ExN*, p. 41, #13)

   In this experiment the children record the climbing-1 facts. As they move the 1-block up the stair, they record each move by making equations with the number markers. Some children may need this practice more than others. (*ExN*, p. 57, #3)

Workbook Page
A. Point out that the stair is the basic structure that the 1-block climbs. Elicit that the 1-block will be added to each step until it climbs to the top and lands on 9. The children write the answers to the examples.

B. The children complete the equation and write equations of their own choice.

$1 + 1 = 2$ $2 + 1 = 3$

$3 + 1 = 4$ $4 + 1 = 5$

$5 + 1 = 6$ $6 + 1 = 7$

Purpose: To discover that adding 1 to a number changes it to the next higher number in the series; that adding 1 to an odd number results in an even number, while adding 1 to an even number results in an odd number.

LESSON 37. Adding 1 to a Number (Pattern Boards)

Group Activity
Give an empty pattern board to each child. Put 1 cube on your display card. Add 1 more cube to it. Ask, "Who has the pattern for 1 and 1? What is its name?" The child with the 2-pattern names it, fills it with your 2 cubes, and puts it in second place in the series. Continue by building the 2-pattern and adding 1 to it. The child with pattern board 3 claims it. Do the same until you reach 9 and 1 equal 10. (*ExN*, p. 30, #3)

   Place the empty pattern boards in sequence. Play the Sticker Game. Tell the children to close their eyes while you hide a sticker under a pattern board, perhaps 7. Have the children open their eyes. Indicate the position of the sticker with the number markers: $6 + 1 =$ ___. A child puts number marker 7 in the equation and finds the sticker under that board. (*ExN*, p. 49, #2)

Workbook Page
The children state the equation shown by the first illustration. Each symbol in the equation records an amount or action depicted in the illustration. The children complete the equations independently.

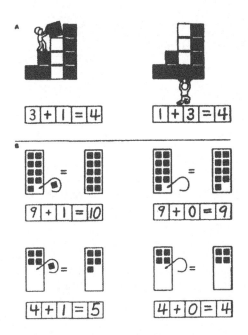

$$3 + 1 = 4 \qquad 1 + 3 = 4$$

$$9 + 1 = 10 \qquad 9 + 0 = 9$$

$$4 + 1 = 5 \qquad 4 + 0 = 4$$

Purpose: To discover that adding any number to 1 has the same result as adding 1 to a number—it is the reverse fact; to learn that adding 0 to a number results in that number.

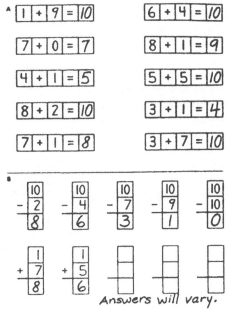

$$1 + 9 = 10 \qquad 6 + 4 = 10$$

$$7 + 0 = 7 \qquad 8 + 1 = 9$$

$$4 + 1 = 5 \qquad 5 + 5 = 10$$

$$8 + 2 = 10 \qquad 3 + 1 = 4$$

$$7 + 1 = 8 \qquad 3 + 7 = 10$$

$$
\begin{array}{ccccc}
10 & 10 & 10 & 10 & 10 \\
-\,2 & -\,4 & -\,7 & -\,9 & -\,10 \\
\hline
8 & 6 & 3 & 1 & 0
\end{array}
$$

$$
\begin{array}{ccccc}
1 & 1 & & & \\
+\,7 & +\,5 & & & \\
\hline
8 & 6 & & &
\end{array}
$$

Answers will vary.

Purpose: To test knowledge of the 10-facts in addition, subtracting from 10, adding 1 or 0 to a number, and adding to 1.

LESSON 38. Adding to 1; Adding 0

Group Activity

Scatter the blocks from the 10-box on the table. Stand a block (such as 6) on end. Place the 1-cube next to 6. Ask, "What do I add to 1 to reach 6?" A child selects the 5-block and states that "1 plus 5 is 6." Elicit that 5 plus 1 is also 6 and is an easier fact to remember. Do the same experiment with other blocks. (*ExN,* p. 57, #4)

Play the Sticker Game. Contrast the addition facts for adding 1 with those for adding 0. Arrange the empty pattern boards in sequence and hide a sticker beneath the 6-board. Give the clue by recording an equation with the number markers: $6 + 0 = $ ___. Elicit that adding 0 means adding nothing else to 6; it remains the same. (*ExN,* p. 49, #2, see *Note*)

Workbook Page

A. Elicit that adding 3 to 1 will give the same result as adding 1 to 3.
B. Go over the facts for adding 0 orally. They are shown in contrast to the facts for adding 1.

LESSON 39. Test: The 10-Facts—Addition and Subtraction; Adding 0; Adding 1; Adding to 1

Group Activity

For a quick and enjoyable review of the 10-facts, play the Scarf Game. Hide the blocks from the 10-box beneath a scarf. Call on children to ask you for a combination that makes 10, which they then place in the 10-box. (*ExN,* p. 38, #8)

For a quick review of adding 1 or adding 0 to numbers, play the Sticker Game. Hide a small sticker beneath a block in the counting board. Give a clue to where it is by recording an equation such as $6 + 0 = $ ___. A child finds the sticker beneath the 6-block and keeps it. (*ExN,* p. 49, #2)

Workbook Page

A. Explain that this test has a mixture of facts in the top section. They are the 10-facts and the facts for adding 1 and adding 0.
B. The children subtract from 10, add to 1, and make up their own facts.

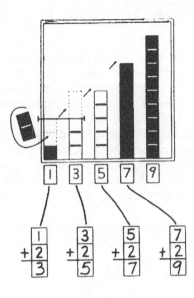

LESSON 40. Adding 2 to Odd Numbers; The Climbing 2

Group Activity

Have the children build a stair with a step of 2. Start the stair with the 1-block. The series will be 1, 3, 5, 7, and 9. Have a child climb up the steps with the 2-block. Elicit that adding 2 to an odd number means skipping the neighbor and reaching the next higher odd number in the series. (*ExN*, p. 41, #14)

Play the Sticker Game in the counting board filled with blocks. Hide a small sticker beneath an odd number block such as 9. Record the clue with the number markers. Say, "The sticker is under the block that is the answer to this example, 7 + 2 = ___." (*ExN*, p. 49, #2)

Workbook Page

Elicit that this stair is made of odd number blocks, 1, 3, 5, 7, and 9. The children draw a line between each block and the example for adding 2 that corresponds to it. The 2-block climbs onto each step in turn. It cannot fit on the 9-block, so there is no example for it. The children complete the examples independently.

Purpose: To discover that when 2 is added to a number, the next number in the series is skipped. Therefore, adding 2 to an odd number results in the next higher odd number.

LESSON 41. Adding 2 to Even Numbers; The Climbing 2

Group Activity

Have the children build the stair with a step of 2. This time start with the 2-block. The series will be 2, 4, 6, 8, and 10. Have a child climb up the steps with an extra 2-block. Elicit that adding 2 to an even number means skipping the neighbor and reaching the next higher even number in the series. (*ExN*, p. 41, #14)

Workbook Page

Elicit that the 2-block is climbing the stair of even number blocks. The children draw a line between each even block and the example that records the climbing 2. The children complete the examples independently.

Purpose: To discover that when 2 is added to a number, the next higher number in the series is skipped. Therefore, adding 2 to an even number results in the next higher even number.

$1+1=2$ $6+1=7$

$2+1=3$ $7+1=8$

$3+1=4$ $8+1=9$

$4+1=5$ $9+1=10$

$5+1=6$

Purpose: To see the facts for adding 1 in a new way and then to contrast adding 1 with adding 2 as it is presented below.

Group Activity

Have the children build the stair in the 10-box and then climb it with the 1-block. Have them recite the fact at each step as they climb up the stair step by step. (*ExN*, p. 41, #13)

Play the Climbing Cat Game. Thinking of a cat climbing up stairs gives children practice in visualizing what has happened when they hear the words, "The cat went up 1 step." Hide the stair of blocks behind a screen. Announce that you have placed a toy cat on a step, such as 3. Say that you have moved the cat "up 1 step" and ask where the cat is now. The child should answer, "4." Remove the screen so the children can see this. Contrast this with having the cat go up 2 steps at a jump. (*ExN*, p. 41, #13B)

Workbook Page

Elicit that the child in the picture is climbing the stairs one at a time. This is a new way to picture the facts for adding 1. The children complete the printed equations and then write the rest of the story of the climbing 1. This is the first time they have been asked to think up all the facts by themselves.

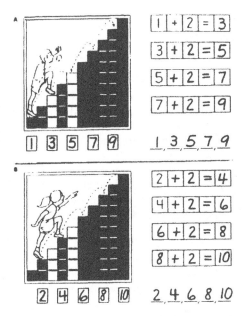

$1+2=3$

$3+2=5$

$5+2=7$

$7+2=9$

1, 3, 5, 7, 9

$2+2=4$

$4+2=6$

$6+2=8$

$8+2=10$

2, 4, 6, 8, 10

Purpose: To see the facts for adding 2 in a different way; to understand completing a sequence of numbers.

LESSON 43. Climbing the Stair with a Step of 2; Completing a Number Sequence

Group Activity

Have the children build the stair in the 10-box. Call on a child to climb it two steps at a time and name the steps—1, 3, 5, 7, and 9 or 2, 4, 6, 8, and 10.

Prepare the children to complete a sequence of numbers by acting out the sequence with blocks. Scatter the blocks on the table. Tell the children you will stand up several blocks in sequence and see whether they can decide what the secret rule is so they can pick the next block. Place the 1-block on the table and follow it with the 3-block. Ask, "What comes next?" A child should pick the 5-block, then the 7-block, and the 9-block. Allow children to be the teacher and begin a sequence of their own.

Workbook Page

A. Elicit that when the child starts on the 1-block, he will step on every other step, which is different from stepping on every step. He steps on the odd number blocks. The children label each odd block in the stair, finish the series of odd numbers, and complete the equations.

B. Elicit that when the child starts on the 2-block, she will step on every other step, or on each even block. The children label each even block in the stair, finish the series of even numbers, and complete the equations.

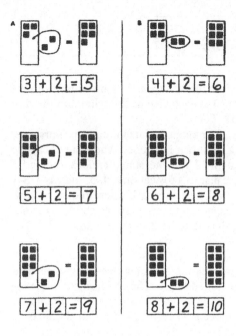

$$3 + 2 = 5 \qquad 4 + 2 = 6$$

$$5 + 2 = 7 \qquad 6 + 2 = 8$$

$$7 + 2 = 9 \qquad 8 + 2 = 10$$

Purpose: To discover that adding 2 to an odd number results in the next higher odd number and adding 2 to an even number results in the next higher even number.

LESSON 44. Adding 2 in the Pattern Boards

Group Activity

Play the Dumping Out Game to review quickly the characteristics of odd and even numbers. Start with all the pattern boards filled with cubes, and in sequence. Call on children to move each odd number board down (1, 3, 5, 7, and 9). Now ask a child to dump out the biggest odd number, another child to dump out the smallest odd number, and so forth. Play the game again by dumping out each even number. (*ExN*, p. 31, #5, #6)

Give each child a display card. Put the empty odd pattern boards in sequence: 1, 3, 5, 7, and 9. On your display card build an odd number, such as 3. Have each child do the same. Now add 2 cubes and have the children do the same thing to their patterns. Elicit that 3 plus 2 equals 5. Call on a child to place his or her cubes into the 5-board and put it in place in the sequence. (*ExN*, p. 32, #7)

Workbook Page

A. Elicit that 2 cubes are being added to odd patterns. Thus, the sum is the next higher odd number.

B. Elicit that 2 cubes are being added to even patterns. Thus, the sum is the next higher even number each time.

The children record each fact in the spaces provided.

A 1 2 3 4 5 6 7 8 9 10

$$\begin{array}{r} 2 \\ +2 \\ \hline 4 \end{array} \quad \begin{array}{r} 4 \\ +2 \\ \hline 6 \end{array} \quad \begin{array}{r} 6 \\ +2 \\ \hline 8 \end{array} \quad \begin{array}{r} 8 \\ +2 \\ \hline 10 \end{array}$$

B 1 2 3 4 5 6 7 8 9 10

$$\begin{array}{r} 1 \\ +2 \\ \hline 3 \end{array} \quad \begin{array}{r} 3 \\ +2 \\ \hline 5 \end{array} \quad \begin{array}{r} 5 \\ +2 \\ \hline 7 \end{array} \quad \begin{array}{r} 7 \\ +2 \\ \hline 9 \end{array}$$

Purpose: To discover that adding 2 to a number results in the next number in the series being skipped. Adding 2 to a sequence of even numbers results in an even number sequence. Adding 2 to a sequence of odd numbers results in an odd number sequence.

LESSON 45. Adding 2 in the Pattern Boards

Group Activity

Play a variation of the Sticker Game. Write on cards the facts for adding 2 to even numbers (0 + 2, 2 + 2, 4 + 2, 6 + 2, and 8 + 2) and then to odd numbers (1 + 2, 3 + 2, 5 + 2, and 7 + 2). Hide stickers under all the empty pattern boards. Shuffle the cards and place them face down on the table. A child draws a card, reads it, names the board where the sticker is hidden, and retrieves the sticker to keep. (*ExN*, p. 49, #2)

Build a number pattern such as 6 on your display card. Elicit that it is even. Move your display card with the 6-pattern behind a screen and add 2 cubes. Let the children see the new pattern. Ask what you did (added 2 cubes). Elicit that 6 + 2 = 8. Do the same to review the odd patterns. (*ExN*, p. 33, #10)

Workbook Page

A. Elicit that when 2 cubes are added to an even number, the next higher even number appears.

B. Elicit that when 2 cubes are added to an odd number, the next higher odd number appears.

The children complete the examples independently.

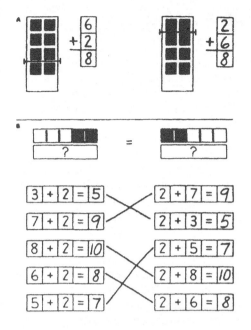

Purpose: To discover that when a number is added to 2, the sum is the same as when 2 is added to that number.

LESSON 46. Adding to 2

Note: Examples such as 2 + 3, 2 + 5, and 2 + 7 are difficult for some children. They are not able to use the idea of the small 2-block climbing up the stair. When they visualize the number patterns, it is too difficult for them to picture a big pattern being added to 2 cubes. Children need only realize that if they reverse the fact, then the familiar fact for adding 2 appears: 2 + 7 = 7 + 2.

Group Activity

Give one child pattern board 6 and have him or her add 2 cubes to it and state the fact. Now give the child's neighbor the 2-board and have him or her add 6 cubes to it and state the fact. Elicit that 6 + 2 has the same sum as 2 + 6.

Review the facts for adding 2 by hiding behind your back two consecutive odd or even number blocks. For example, hide 5 and 7. Show the smaller block. Announce, "The hidden block is 2 bigger than 5; what is it?" The child who answers should take the next turn as teacher.

Workbook Page

A. Elicit that 6 + 2 and 2 + 6 have the same sum. The children complete the examples.

B. The familiar facts are on the left. The children draw a line to connect each fact to its reverse fact and write the answers in the boxes.

A 9 + 1 = 10   2 + 8 = 10

7 + 3 = 10   4 + 6 = 10

5 + 5 = 10   6 + 4 = 10

3 + 7 = 10   8 + 2 = 10

1 + 9 = 10   10 + 0 = 10

B

6	3	7	5	4
+ 2	+ 2	+ 2	+ 2	+ 2
8	5	9	7	6

2	2	2	2	2
+ 6	+ 3	+ 7	+ 5	+ 4
8	5	9	7	6

Purpose: To test mastery of the 10-facts and the facts for adding 2 and adding to 2.

LESSON 47. Test: The 10-Facts; Adding 2; Adding to 2

Group Activity

To review the 10-facts, play a new game similar to Memory, or Concentration. Paste an index card over the back of each pattern board to cover the see-through pattern on it. Turn the pattern boards face down and scatter them around. A player turns up a pattern such as 7, names it, and announces that 7 needs the 3-pattern to make 10. If she or he turns it up, the two pattern boards make a book. If not, both pattern boards are turned face down for another pupil to use. This game helps children remember these two difficult facts: the even fact, 6 + 4 = 10, and the odd fact, 7 + 3 = 10. (New Game)

Play the Sticker Game. Arrange the empty pattern boards in sequence. Hide a sticker under one of them. With the number markers record an example for adding 2 that tells the player where to find the sticker: 6 + 2 = ___. (*ExN*, p. 49, #2)

Workbook Page

A. This is the last test on the 10-facts in addition.

B. Facts for adding 2 and adding to 2 are tested.

The children complete the test independently.

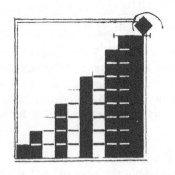

$|10| - |1| = |9|$ $\quad$ $|5| - |1| = |4|$

$|9| - |1| = |8|$ $\quad$ $|4| - |1| = |3|$

$|8| - |1| = |7|$ $\quad$ $|3| - |1| = |2|$

$|7| - |1| = |6|$ $\quad$ $|2| - |1| = |1|$

$|6| - |1| = |5|$ $\quad$ $|1| - |1| = |0|$

Purpose: To realize that subtracting 1 from a number means reaching the next smaller number in the series.

LESSON 48. Subtracting 1

Group Activity

To answer facts for subtracting 1 quickly, children must be able to say the number sequence backwards from 10 to 1. Build the stair from 1 to 10. For some children it is important to go up the stair by moving from left to right and down the stair by moving from right to left. As they descend the stair, they say each number name. Play the game Which Step is Missing? Hide a block. Say that the missing step is one smaller than 6. (*ExN*, p. 19, #5)

In the counting board play the Stand Up Game. Ask a child to "Stand up 10 and the block equal to 10 minus 1." Give the next children similar orders. When all the blocks are standing up, say, "Put down 10 and the block one less than 10," until all the blocks are down again. (*ExN*, p. 23, #2)

Workbook Page

Explain that subtracting 1 as shown in this illustration can't be done with the Structural Arithmetic materials. The children have to *imagine* that by taking 1 cube from the 10-block they would have a block equal to the next smaller block, 9. This is, of course, true of subtracting 1 from any block. The children finish writing the equations by themselves.

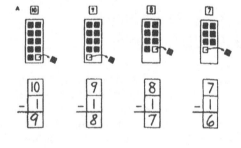

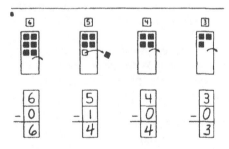

Purpose: To realize that subtracting 1 from a number changes it to the next smaller number; to discover that subtracting 1 from an even number results in an odd number and subtracting 1 from an odd number results in an even number; to realize that subtracting zero from a number leaves the number unchanged.

LESSON 49. Subtracting 0 Contrasted with Subtracting 1

Group Activity

Give each child an empty pattern board. On your display card build a pattern with cubes (perhaps 10). Say, "I subtract 1 cube." As you do so, ask, "What is it now?" Call on the child with the 9-board to state the equation, 10 minus 1 equals 9. She or he fills the pattern board with cubes and puts it in place in the sequence. (*ExN*, p. 30, #4)

Play the Sticker Game by arranging the pattern boards from 1 to 10 in sequence. Hide a sticker beneath the 3-board. Give a clue to the children by using the number markers to form an example: $4 - 1 = $ __ or $3 - 0 = $ __. The child who knows the answer looks under the 3-board and claims the sticker. (*ExN*, p. 49, #2)

Workbook Page

A. Elicit that one cube is being subtracted from each pattern. The children write the answers in the boxes.

B. Elicit that when no cube is subtracted, the pattern remains unchanged. Remind the children how to record subtracting 0 in the last two examples.

$$10 - 2 = 8$$
$$8 - 2 = 6$$
$$6 - 2 = 4$$
$$4 - 2 = 2$$
$$2 - 2 = 0$$

1 2 3 4 5 6 7 8 9 1

$$\begin{array}{r} 10 \\ -\ 2 \\ \hline 8 \end{array}$$

Purpose: To discover that subtracting 2 from an even number means skipping the neighbor and reaching the next lower even number.

LESSON 50. Descending the Stair with a Step of 2

Group Activity

Have the children build a stair of even number blocks 2, 4, 6, 8, and 10. Have each name recited as a child uses his or her forefinger to climb the stair, and the sequence recited in reverse as the finger descends the stair. Cover the stair with a notebook. Reveal the 10-block. Ask, "What is 10 minus 2?" When the next even block, 8, has been named, slide the notebook back and reveal it. Keep on until the fact $2 - 2 = 0$ is asked. (*ExN*, p. 37, #6)

Play the Climbing Cat Game. Have the children build the stair from 1 to 10 in the 10-box. Place a toy cat on a step such as 6. Place a screen before it. Say, "The cat is on step 6; it jumps down 2 steps. Where is it now?" After a child names the step, remove the screen as a check; there is the cat on 4. (*ExN*, p. 41, #13B, #14B)

Workbook Page

A. Discuss the boy descending the stairs two at a time. Elicit that since he started on 10, he will step only on the even numbered steps, 10, 8, 6, 4, and 2. The children finish the equations independently.

B. Ask what subtraction story can be told about the birds. This problem shows the "take away" concept of subtraction. The children complete the example.

$$9 - 2 = 7$$
$$7 - 2 = 5$$
$$5 - 2 = 3$$
$$3 - 2 = 1$$

1 3 5 7 9

$$5 - 2 = 3$$

Purpose: To discover that subtracting 2 from an odd number means skipping the neighbor and reaching the next lower odd number.

LESSON 51. Descending the Stair with a Step of 2

Group Activity

Place the odd number blocks, 1, 3, 5, 7, and 9 on a table across the room. Display the empty counting board. Tell a child to get 9 and the block that is 2 less than 9. When the blocks are put in place in the board, the children are reminded in a new way that subtracting 2 from an odd number skips the neighbor and equals the next lower odd number. (*ExN*, p. 25, #6)

Place the climbing cat on any odd number block in the stair. Conceal it behind a screen. Say, "The cat is on step 9; it went down 2 steps. On which block is it now?" Reveal the cat when they have answered, "The 7-block." (*ExN*, p. 41, #13B, #14B)

Workbook Page

A. Discuss the girl descending the stairs two at a time. Ask what block she started on and what blocks she will therefore step on when going down the stairs (the odd number blocks, 9, 7, 5, 3, and 1). The children finish the equations independently.

B. The "take away" aspect of subtraction is shown in this picture. The children state the problem in their own words and then finish writing the equation.

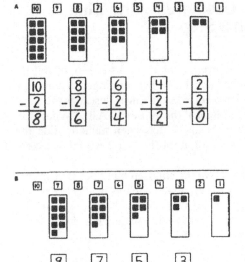

Purpose: To discover that subtracting 2 from a number means skipping the neighbor and reaching the next lower number; to discover that subtracting 2 from an even number pattern changes it to the next smaller even pattern and that subtracting 2 from an odd number pattern changes it to the next smaller odd pattern.

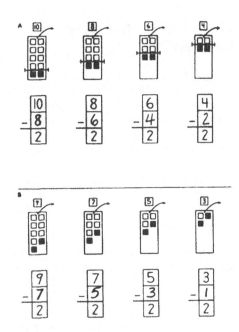

Purpose: To discover that there is always a remainder of 2 when an even number is subtracted from the next higher even number and when an odd number is subtracted from the next higher odd number.

LESSON 52. Subtracting 2 in the Pattern Boards

Group Activity

Give each child a different pattern board. On your display card build the 10-pattern with cubes of one color. Subtract 2 cubes. Ask, "What did I do?" Ask, "Who has this board?" The child with the 8-board states the equation, "10 minus 2 equals 8" and puts the 8-board in place on the cardboard strip in the series from 1 to 10. (*ExN*, p 32, #8)

Build the 10-pattern with cubes of one color on your display card. Say, "10 take away 2" as you remove the 2 cubes from the bottom row. The children see the 8-pattern and name it. Take 2 cubes from the 8-pattern. A child answers the question, "8 minus 2?" by naming the 6-pattern. Continue until you ask, "2 minus 2?" A child answers, "Zero." (New Game)

Workbook Page

A. Elicit that the pattern boards make up a series of even patterns. The children read the example beneath each even pattern board and explain that the answer is the next lower even pattern since there is a difference of 2 between consecutive even patterns. The children write the answers.
B. Elicit that this is a series of odd patterns. The children explain that taking 2 cubes from an odd number gives the next lower odd number. They write the answers.

LESSON 53. A Remainder of 2 in the Pattern Boards

Group Activity

Arrange the even pattern boards in sequence—2, 4, 6, 8, and 10. Ask a child how many cubes on the 10-board you should cover with an index card so that only the bottom 2 remain visible. If necessary, indicate that it is the amount of the next lower even number, and thus cover 8 of the 10 cubes. Elicit that 10 minus 8 equals 2. Continue with the other even boards. (New Game)

Play a variation of the Screen Game. Show the children pattern board 10 filled with 10 cubes. Then place it behind a screen and ask the children, "How many cubes should I subtract so only 2 will be left?" They should answer, "Subtract 8 cubes!" Do so behind the screen, and then show them the remainder of 2 cubes. (*ExN*, p. 33, #10)

Workbook Page

A. Elicit that the number patterns at the top of the page are even. Let the children discover that in each example the amount of the next lower even number must be subtracted in order to leave a remainder of 2 cubes. They write this number in the space provided in each example.
B. Elicit that these number patterns are odd. The children must, therefore, subtract the next lower odd number each time to leave a remainder of 2 cubes. They write the number in the space provided in each example.

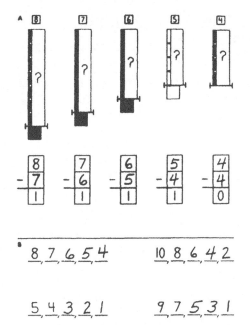

$$\begin{array}{ccccc} 8 & 7 & 6 & 5 & 4 \\ -7 & -6 & -5 & -4 & -4 \\ \hline 1 & 1 & 1 & 1 & 0 \end{array}$$

*   8, 7, 6, 5, 4   10, 8, 6, 4, 2

    5, 4, 3, 2, 1   9, 7, 5, 3, 1

Purpose: To realize that to have a remainder of 1, the next smaller number is subtracted from any number in the series; to have a remainder of 0, the number must be subtracted from itself.

LESSON 54. A Remainder of 1; A Remainder of 0; Completing Number Sequences

Group Activity
Fill each groove of the counting board with cubes of one color to make mock blocks of cubes. Put the corresponding number marker above each mock block. Point to 10. Ask, "How many cubes must I subtract from 10 so that only 1 cube will remain?" (you may cover the subtracted number with a strip of paper). Elicit that you are always subtracting the amount of the next smaller block to get a remainder of 1. (New Game)

Workbook Page
A. The children tell you how they figure out the name of the unknown block in each example. They should recognize the pictured block, such as 8, and figure out the name of the mystery block because they can see that it is 1 less than 8 (the 7-block). Point out what happens in order to have a remainder of 0. The children complete the equations independently.

B. Remind the children how to finish a sequence of numbers. Point out that the first sequence is the name of each block at the top of the page. They complete the sequences independently.

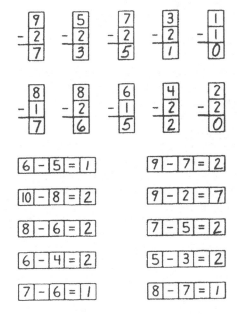

$$\begin{array}{ccccc} 9 & 5 & 7 & 3 & 1 \\ -2 & -2 & -2 & -2 & -1 \\ \hline 7 & 3 & 5 & 1 & 0 \end{array}$$

$$\begin{array}{ccccc} 8 & 8 & 6 & 4 & 2 \\ -1 & -2 & -1 & -2 & -2 \\ \hline 7 & 6 & 5 & 2 & 0 \end{array}$$

6 − 5 = 1	9 − 7 = 2
10 − 8 = 2	9 − 2 = 7
8 − 6 = 2	7 − 5 = 2
6 − 4 = 2	5 − 3 = 2
7 − 6 = 1	8 − 7 = 1

Purpose: To review the subtraction combinations that leave a remainder of 0, 1, or 2; to review subtracting 1 or 2 from a number.

LESSON 55. Test: Subtracting 1; Subtracting 2; A Remainder of 0, 1, or 2

Group Activity
Review subtracting 1 and subtracting 2 by playing the Sticker Game with the pattern boards. Write an equation that tells where the sticker is hidden. Use only facts for subtracting 1 or subtracting 2. Call on a child to read the equation and retrieve the sticker. (*ExN*, p. 49, #2)

Slap Jack gives practice in reading examples with a remainder of 1 or 2. Make two sets of cards on which are written the following examples with a remainder of 2:

10	9	8	7	6	5	4	3	2
−8	−7	−6	−5	−4	−3	−2	−1	−0

Remind children that there is a remainder of 2 between consecutive odd or even numbers. Make two sets of cards on which are written the following examples with a remainder of 1:

10	9	8	7	6	5	4	3	2	1
−9	−8	−7	−6	−5	−4	−3	−2	−1	−0

Combine all four sets of cards. Place half the shuffled deck face down in front of each of two players. The players sit beside each other and each turns up a card simultaneously. If 2 is the answer to both cards, the first child to slap both cards wins them and the cards beneath them. If a child slaps the cards when the answer to both is *not* 2, he or she forfeits the cards to the other player. Elicit that examples with consecutive numbers have an answer of 1. They are easy to spot. This increases children's speed in reading examples. (New Game)

Workbook Page
The children complete the page independently.

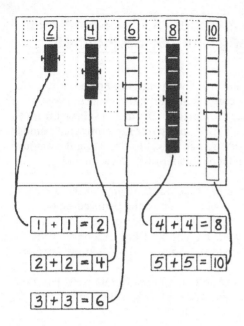

Purpose: To realize that when each number from 1 to 5 is doubled, the sums are the even numbers, 2, 4, 6, 8, and 10.

LESSON 56. The Doubles in the Counting Board

Group Activity
Present the empty counting board. Scatter on the table two each of blocks 1 to 5. Ask each child to select "two blocks the same size." Tell them we call these the doubles. Place an even number marker such as 10 in the counting board. Ask, "Who has two numbers the same size that together make 10? Put them in this groove." (Point to the 10-groove.) The child with two 5-blocks puts them in the 10-groove and tells us that 5 and 5 make 10. Continue filling the other even numbered grooves. (New Game)

Play the Hiding Game. Have the children close their eyes. Hide two equal blocks behind your back. Now say, "Ready! Together my two blocks make 8. They are the same size as each other." Children should know you have 4 and 4. Let the children take the role of teacher in this game. (*ExN*, p. 39, #9)

Workbook Page
The children go over all the doubles and recite the facts orally. They must draw a line from the double blocks in the counting board to each fact in equation form below. The children complete the page independently.

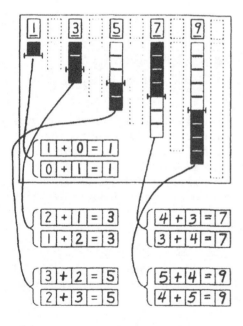

Purpose: To discover that the sum of two consecutive numbers is always an odd number.

Note: The name "consecutive numbers" means numbers that follow one another in descending or ascending order in the number series. They are also referred to as "neighbors," or "numbers that live next to each other." As long as you use them consistently, it doesn't matter which of the terms you choose.

LESSON 57. Adding Consecutive Numbers in the Counting Board

Group Activity
Have the children build a stair from 1 to 10 in the 10-box. Demonstrate the new vocabulary in the following way. Select two consecutive number blocks such as 1 and 2, and tell the children they are called consecutive numbers (or neighbors, or numbers that live next to each other in the stair). Give each child a chance to select two consecutive numbers. They will be (1, 2), (3, 4), (5, 6), (7, 8), and (9, 10). Then build another stair from 2 to 9. This time the sets of consecutive numbers will be (2, 3), (4, 5), (6, 7), and (8, 9). Display the counting board. Put an odd number marker such as 5 in place. Ask, "Who has two consecutive numbers that together make 5?" The child who has 2 and 3 places them in the 5-groove. Elicit that this could also be 3 and 2 make 5. Have the children fill the grooves for the odd numbers 3, 5, 7, and 9. Explain that the consecutive numbers that make 1 are 0 and 1. (Blocks 6 to 10 are too large because the sum of double 6 is 12 and of neighbors 5 and 6 is 11.) (New Game)

Play the Scarf Game. Hide two sets of blocks 1 to 5 beneath a scarf. Turn the odd number markers face down. The child who draws number marker 9 must ask for the two neighbors that equal 9: "Please give me blocks 4 and 5." When you give the child the blocks, he or she puts them into the 9-groove in the counting board. Continue with the others. (*ExN*, p. 38, #8)

Workbook Page
The children go over the consecutive numbers that make up each odd number, reciting the reverse fact each time. They draw a line from the blocks in the counting board to the two equations that record these blocks. They complete the equations independently.

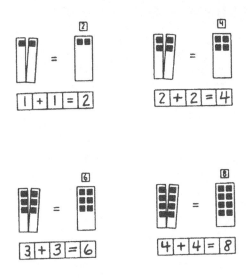

$$1 + 1 = 2 \qquad 2 + 2 = 4$$

$$3 + 3 = 6 \qquad 4 + 4 = 8$$

Purpose: To realize in a different presentation that even numbers are doubles and consist of two equal parts.

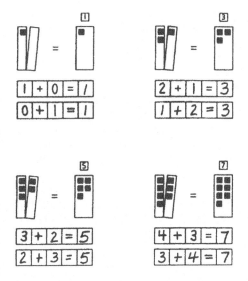

$$1 + 0 = 1 \qquad 2 + 1 = 3$$
$$0 + 1 = 1 \qquad 1 + 2 = 3$$

$$3 + 2 = 5 \qquad 4 + 3 = 7$$
$$2 + 3 = 5 \qquad 3 + 4 = 7$$

Purpose: To realize by a different presentation that the sum of two consecutive numbers is an odd number.

LESSON 58. The Doubles in the Pattern Boards

Group Activity

Arrange the even pattern boards in sequence on the table. Show how each even pattern can be split down the center. For example, place a pencil down the center of the 6-pattern board. Using two paper cups, put 3 cubes of one color in one cup and 3 cubes of a different color in the other cup. As you dump out each cup, have a child name the number (3), and then the total (6). Call on a child to state that 3 and 3 make 6, and to put the cubes into the proper pattern board. Continue with other even patterns in the same way. (*ExN*, p. 51, #5)

Play the Hiding Game. Display all the pattern boards with the proper number marker above each board. When the children's eyes are closed, select the cubes for a double, such as 8. Now put 4 cubes in one hand and 4 different colored cubes in the other. Announce that you have 8 in all. Ask what is in each hand. The child who guesses gets the cubes to put into the board. (*ExN*, p. 52, #7)

Workbook Page

Each even pattern has been split evenly into two parts. The children record the number of cubes beneath each part. Then they write the total after the equal sign. They finish the equations independently.

LESSON 59. Adding Consecutive Numbers in the Pattern Boards

Group Activity

Arrange the odd pattern boards in sequence. Show how each odd pattern can be split by placing a pencil down the center of the board. Now place the cubes for one of the patterns, for instance 7, into two cups. Put 4 cubes of one color in one cup and 3 cubes of a different color in the other. As you dump out the cubes, have a child name the number (4), then the other number (3), and then the total (7). The children find pattern board 7 and recite the fact, 4 and 3 are 7, and put the cubes into that board. (*ExN*, p. 51, #6)

Play a Sticker Game. Print the combinations of consecutive numbers on cards. A child selects a card, reads the example, 4 + 3, and retrieves the sticker beneath the 7-board. (*ExN*, p. 52, #8)

Workbook Page

Each odd pattern has been split into two parts. Explain that they cannot be the same size. The children record the number beneath each part. Then they write the total and the reverse fact.

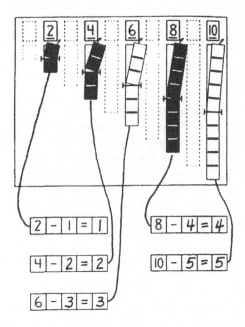

2 − 1 = 1

4 − 2 = 2

6 − 3 = 3

8 − 4 = 4

10 − 5 = 5

Purpose: To discover the result when one of two like parts is subtracted from a double.

LESSON 60. Subtracting from Doubles

Group Activity

Display the empty counting board and give each child two like blocks from 1 to 5. Call back these combinations of doubles. For example, put number marker 8 above the 8-groove. Ask, "Who has two blocks the same that make 8?" The child who has the two 4-blocks places them in the 8-groove and states, "4 and 4 equal 8." When all the doubles are in place, elicit that these are the even numbers. Now cover the blocks that make 8 with a piece of paper. Call on a child. Say, "I have 8 altogether. If I subtract 4 (withdraw the 4-block), what remains?" Once the answer has been given, remove the paper to reveal the "remainder" of 4 and have a child state the subtraction fact, "8 minus 4 is 4." (New Game)

Play the Scarf Game. Ask children to close their eyes. Hide two like blocks under a scarf. Say, "Open. I have hidden 8 altogether. If Ann takes 4 away, what will be left?" Ann withdraws a 4-block. The children announce that the other 4-block is left. Let them look under the scarf. They should state the subtraction fact, "8 take away 4 leaves 4." (*ExN*, p. 58, #5)

Workbook Page

The children connect the pictured block combination with the equation that records it by drawing a line between them. They finish the equations independently.

1 − 1 = 0

1 − 0 = 1

3 − 2 = 1

3 − 1 = 2

5 − 3 = 2

5 − 2 = 3

7 − 4 = 3

7 − 3 = 4

9 − 5 = 4

9 − 4 = 5

Purpose: To discover the result when one of the two consecutive numbers that makes up an odd number is subtracted from it.

LESSON 61. Subtracting from Odd Numbers

Group Activity

Display the empty counting board with the even number markers in place, 2, 4, 6, 8, and 10. Have the children put in place the blocks for the doubles as shown in Lesson 60. Next, remove number markers 2 and 4 and turn them face down in place. Put marker 3 in place between them. Say, "We know that 1 and 1 make 2" (move one of the 1-blocks into the 3-groove). Ask, "What does 1 need to make 3?" Show how the 2-block from the neighboring double (4) can be moved to the left into the 3-groove to join the 1-block to make 3. Continue showing that each odd number can be made up by part of the double on each side of it. The children will enjoy this. It gives new insight into the relationship between doubles and neighbors. This demonstration brings out the point that the knowledge of the doubles helps one to figure out the sums of the neighbors. (New Game)

When the children's eyes are closed, place two consecutive blocks with a total of 9 or less beneath a box, for example, 3 and 4. Say, "Ready! I have two neighbors, or consecutive numbers, under this box. They make 7 in all. If I subtract 3 (withdraw it from under the box), what block remains?" The children should name the 4-block, and lift up the box to reveal it. They should state the subtraction fact and put both blocks into the 7-groove. (*ExN*, p. 58, #6)

Workbook Page

Elicit that each odd number will have two facts recorded below it because the blocks are not the same. You can first take one away, then the other one. The children draw a line between each combination pictured and the corresponding two facts. The children complete the page independently.

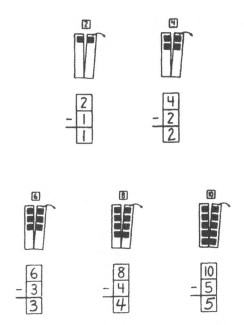

Purpose: To see the result when one of the two equal parts is subtracted from a double.

LESSON 62. Subtracting from Doubles in the Pattern Boards

Group Activity

Arrange the even pattern boards in sequence and have the children fill each board using cubes of two different colors so they show the doubles $1 + 1$, $2 + 2$, $3 + 3$, $4 + 4$, and $5 + 5$. Give each child one of these filled pattern boards and show them how to tell a subtraction story using the board they have been given. They should use the following form: "My dog had 6 puppies. I gave 3 away (show this with the cubes). I have 3 left for myself." (*ExN*, p. 53, #9)

Take the even boards and some cubes. Fill only the left side of the two equal parts as shown in the workbook. Make a set of cards with equations or examples in column form for each even board. Place the half-filled boards on a table across the room. Have a child select a card, for example, $2 - 1 = \_\_$. Instruct him or her to read it, "2 minus 1 equals what?" and go to the table to find the board that shows 2 with 1 cube missing. (New Game)

Workbook Page

The children finish each example independently.

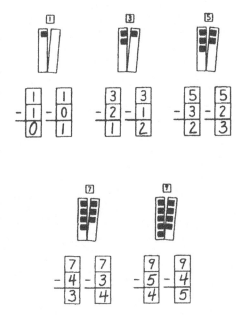

Purpose: To see the result when one of the two consecutive numbers that makes up an odd number is subtracted from that number.

LESSON 63. Subtracting from Odd Numbers in the Pattern Boards

Group Activity

Arrange the odd pattern boards in sequence and have the children fill each board with cubes of two colors so they demonstrate the sums of consecutive numbers: $1 + 0$, $2 + 1$, $3 + 2$, $4 + 3$, and $5 + 4$. (*ExN*, p. 51, #6)

Give each child one of these odd pattern boards so they can act out a subtraction story you tell. They will hear several numbers, but must learn to picture the events of the story so they will know which board can be used to act it out. (*ExN*, p. 53, #10)

Play the Screen Game. Fill one of the odd pattern boards with cubes. When you have moved it behind the screen, subtract one of the rows. Show the remainder and ask the children to say what you did: "You had 7 cubes. You took 3 cubes away, and 4 are left." (*ExN*, p. 54, #11)

Workbook Page

Elicit that for each odd number, you can have two subtraction facts. Because the two parts are different, you can subtract first one of them and then the other from the total. The children finish the page independently.

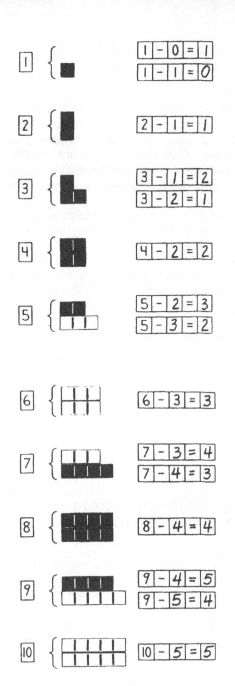

Purpose: To see the result when one of two equal parts is subtracted from an even number, or when one of two consecutive numbers is subtracted from an odd number.

LESSONS 64 and 65. Subtracting from Odd and Even Numbers

Group Activity

Scatter on the table all three sets of blocks 1 to 5—two sets from the 10-box and one set from the counting board. Using cubes from the 10-box with 100 cubes, construct another set of blocks 1 to 4. Tape the cubes together if you wish. Arrange the even number markers 2, 4, 6, 8, and 10 in sequence from left to right on the table. Have a child choose a number, perhaps the 6-marker, and place side by side beneath this marker the two 3-blocks that make up 6. (They should be placed vertically, not horizontally as in the workbook.) The child should state, "3 and 3 make 6." Continue until a double, or pair of like blocks, lies below each even number marker. Next, place an odd number marker between each even number marker. Have the children place beneath each odd number the two consecutive blocks that make up that number: $1 + 0 = 1$, $2 + 1 = 3$, $3 + 2 = 5$, $4 + 3 = 7$, and $5 + 4 = 9$. The result will be similar to the layout for Lessons 64 and 65 but will be arranged vertically. Use this display to play the game described below.

Leave the number blocks arranged as follows: doubles beneath the even numbers and neighbors beneath the odd numbers, as described above. On cards or dominoes write the equations that belong to Lessons 64 and 65. Shuffle the pile and turn it face down. Have the children take turns reading an equation and placing it beneath the pair of blocks it records. This gives them a deeper understanding of the combinations that make up the odd and even numbers. We call these combinations the doubles and neighbors.

Workbook Page

The children complete the equations in Lessons 64 and 65 independently.

$3 + 2 = 5$
$2 + 3 = 5$

$5 - 2 = 3$
$5 - 3 = 2$

$3 + 3 = 6$
$6 - 3 = 3$

Purpose: To present addition and subtraction as different ways of thinking about any two component parts of a number.

LESSON 66. The Interrelationship between Addition and Subtraction

Group Activity
Demonstrate the commutative property of 5 by getting two 2-blocks and two 3-blocks and standing the two combinations side by side, $3 + 2$ and $2 + 3$. Have the children state both facts. Ask who can figure out one related subtraction fact for each addition fact. Explain that for every two component parts of a number there are two addition facts and two subtraction facts, except in the case of the doubles. Show why the doubles have only two facts, one addition fact and one subtraction fact.

Workbook Page
A. The children complete the equations independently.
B. Elicit why there are only two facts. (If you reverse $3 + 3$, you get the same fact.)

A

$4 + 3 = 7$
$3 + 4 = 7$

$7 - 4 = 3$
$7 - 3 = 4$

B

$4 + 4 = 8$
$8 - 4 = 4$

C

$\boxed{+} ~ \text{or} ~ \boxed{-} ~ ?$

$4 + 5 = 9$
$9 - 5 = 4$

$9 - 4 = 5$
$5 + 4 = 9$

Purpose: To present addition and subtraction as different ways of thinking about any two component parts of a number.

LESSON 67. The Interrelationship between Addition and Subtraction

Group Activity
Play a variation of the Scarf Game to test knowledge of the facts for the doubles and neighbors. Tell the children you have hidden beneath the scarf two sets of neighbors, or consecutive numbers, that make 7. See whether they can figure out two different addition facts orally; then take out blocks $4 + 3$, then $3 + 4$. Have the children state two related subtraction facts, $7 - 4 = 3$ and $7 - 3 = 4$. Do the same for several other odd numbers and a few even numbers. (*ExN*, p. 38, #8)

Play the Screen Game. Fill pattern board 7 with cubes. Pass it behind a screen and remove 3 cubes. Reveal the diminished pattern. Ask, "What did I do, add or subtract? Show me by getting the right sign." The children see that 3 cubes are missing and use the number marker for minus to record $7 - 3 = 4$. Do the same for other odd numbers. (*ExN*, p. 54, #12)

Workbook Page
A. Elicit that 7 is an odd number and therefore has two addition facts and two subtraction facts.
B. Elicit that the double 8 has only two related facts, while the numbers 7 and 9 are odd and have four related facts each.
C. This corresponds to the screen game just described.
The children finish the page independently.

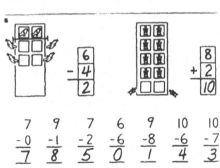

$$
\begin{array}{ccccccc}
5 & 4 & 3 & 3 & 2 & 4 & 3 \\
+5 & +4 & +3 & +4 & +1 & +5 & +2 \\
\hline
10 & 8 & 6 & 7 & 3 & 9 & 5
\end{array}
$$

$$
\begin{array}{ccccccc}
5 & 0 & 2 & 4 & 2 & 1 & 1 \\
+4 & +1 & +2 & +3 & +3 & +2 & +1 \\
\hline
9 & 1 & 4 & 7 & 5 & 3 & 2
\end{array}
$$

$$
\begin{array}{ccccccc}
10 & 8 & 7 & 5 & 9 & 3 & 6 \\
-5 & -4 & -3 & -2 & -4 & -2 & -3 \\
\hline
5 & 4 & 4 & 3 & 5 & 1 & 3
\end{array}
$$

$$
\begin{array}{ccccccc}
4 & 1 & 7 & 5 & 9 & 3 & 1 \\
-2 & -1 & -4 & -3 & -5 & -1 & -0 \\
\hline
2 & 0 & 3 & 2 & 4 & 2 & 1
\end{array}
$$

Purpose: To test the addition and subtraction facts for doubles and neighbors.

$$
\begin{array}{ccccccc}
4 & 1 & 0 & 7 & 5 & 4 & 2 \\
+2 & +7 & +4 & +3 & +2 & +6 & +7 \\
\hline
6 & 8 & 4 & 10 & 7 & 10 & 9
\end{array}
$$

$$
\begin{array}{ccccccc}
6 & 3 & 7 & 6 & 2 & 6 & 5 \\
+2 & +7 & +2 & +4 & +6 & +1 & +0 \\
\hline
8 & 10 & 9 & 10 & 8 & 7 & 5
\end{array}
$$

$$
\begin{array}{ccccccc}
7 & 9 & 7 & 6 & 9 & 10 & 10 \\
-0 & -1 & -2 & -6 & -8 & -6 & -7 \\
\hline
7 & 8 & 5 & 0 & 1 & 4 & 3
\end{array}
$$

Purpose: To test the 10-facts; adding 0, 1, and 2; adding to 0, to 1, and to 2; and related subtraction facts.

LESSON 68. Test: Doubles and Neighbors

Group Activity

To review these facts, display the counting board and scatter on the table three sets of blocks 1 to 5 and another set of blocks 1 to 4 constructed from single cubes. Have the children put the doubles combinations in place in the even numbered grooves, 2, 4, 6, 8, and 10. Have them put a 1-block in the 1-groove and then pairs of consecutive blocks in the rest of the odd numbered grooves, 3, 5, 7, and 9. (Explain that the neighbors that make 1 are 0 and 1.)

Play the game What Comes Next? Cover all the combinations of blocks with a piece of cardboard or an open notebook. Reveal the 10-groove and have a child state the two related facts: 5 + 5 = 10 and 10 − 5 = 5. Ask, "What comes next?" Tell them that there are two consecutive blocks that make 9. They should state four related facts: 4 + 5 = 9, 5 + 4 = 9, 9 − 5 = 4, and 9 − 4 = 5. Now draw back the cardboard cover and reveal the blocks that make 9. The combinations are thus reviewed in one of the contexts in which they were learned, which is important. (*ExN*, p. 37, #6)

Workbook Page

The children first go over the page orally and then take the test.
A. Facts for adding doubles and neighbors are tested.
B. Facts for subtracting from doubles and neighbors are tested.

LESSON 69. Test: The 10-Facts; Adding 0, 1, and 2; Adding to 0, to 1, and to 2

Note: These examples include the four most difficult 10-facts (6 + 4, 4 + 6, 7 + 3, and 3 + 7), and just a sampling of the following facts: adding 0, adding to 0, adding 1, adding to 1, adding 2, adding to 2, and several corresponding subtraction facts.

Group Activity

The 10-facts can be quickly reviewed by playing What Comes Next?, using the 10-box. Cover the filled 10-box with a notebook. See whether the children can recite each fact before you reveal the combinations of blocks, one after another. (*ExN*, p. 37, #6)

Adding 2 to odd and even numbers can be reviewed by arranging the empty boards in sequence from 1 to 10. Move the even pattern boards down a tiny bit so they stand out from the odd pattern boards. Let each pupil select 2 cubes and add them to any pattern and state the combination. (They should add the cubes below the blanks of each pattern as in Lessons 44 and 45.) Do the same with adding 1 cube, then no cubes or zero, each time having the child state the combination. This could be played by two teams. Players take turns tossing a stop-and-go cube (color two sides of a large die red and the other four sides green). If the cube lands on "go," the player adds 2 cubes to a pattern board and writes the example on the chalkboard for her or his team.

Workbook Page

Go over the page orally.
A. The children complete the examples as a test.
B. The children discuss the story problems if necessary.

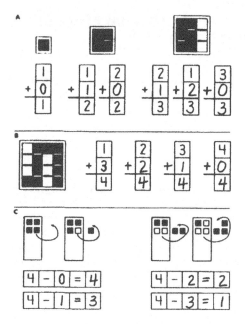

$\dfrac{\begin{array}{r}1\\+\,0\end{array}}{1}$ $\dfrac{\begin{array}{r}1\\+\,1\end{array}}{2}$ $\dfrac{\begin{array}{r}2\\+\,0\end{array}}{2}$ $\dfrac{\begin{array}{r}2\\+\,1\end{array}}{3}$ $\dfrac{\begin{array}{r}1\\+\,2\end{array}}{3}$ $\dfrac{\begin{array}{r}3\\+\,0\end{array}}{3}$

$\dfrac{\begin{array}{r}1\\+\,3\end{array}}{4}$ $\dfrac{\begin{array}{r}2\\+\,2\end{array}}{4}$ $\dfrac{\begin{array}{r}3\\+\,1\end{array}}{4}$ $\dfrac{\begin{array}{r}4\\+\,0\end{array}}{4}$

$4 - 0 = 4$ $4 - 2 = 2$

$4 - 1 = 3$ $4 - 3 = 1$

Purpose: To discover and write the combinations that make 1, 2, 3, and 4 and the facts for subtracting from 4.

LESSON 70. Combinations That Make 1, 2, 3, and 4; Subtracting from 4

Note: The children should begin systematically studying the combinations of blocks in each number box. The number combinations that can be discovered in these boxes form an excellent organization of the 55 basic addition facts (see the table on page 10). Going through the number boxes is a good review. Remember, only one block is needed to fill the whole row in each box. For example, when filling the 4-box, children need only one 4-block.

Group Activity

Let the children fit the number boxes together into a pyramid or arrange them in sequence from the 1-box to the 10-box. Now, select just boxes 1 to 4. Have the children fill each box with blocks. Elicit that there is only one fact for the 1-box: (1 + 0 = 1). Let the children discover the two facts that make 2 (1 + 1 = 2 and 2 + 0 = 2). Go on with the 3-box and the 4-box. It might be fun to play the Hiding Game with the blocks in each box. Display the 4-box, for example, and hide two blocks, such as 3 and 1. Say, "Open your eyes! I have 4 altogether. In one hand is 3. What is in my other hand?" Let the children be the teacher. They enjoy this game. (*ExN*, p. 39, #9; p. 40, #11)

Workbook Page

A and **B.** The children record the facts for each number box.
C. The subtraction facts are shown with the pattern boards. The children complete each equation.

$\dfrac{\begin{array}{r}1\\+\,4\end{array}}{5}$ $\dfrac{\begin{array}{r}2\\+\,3\end{array}}{5}$ $\dfrac{\begin{array}{r}3\\+\,2\end{array}}{5}$ $\dfrac{\begin{array}{r}4\\+\,1\end{array}}{5}$ $\dfrac{\begin{array}{r}5\\+\,0\end{array}}{5}$

$5 - \underline{4} = 1$ $5 - \underline{1} = 4$

$5 - \underline{3} = 2$ $5 - \underline{2} = 3$

$5 - \underline{5} = 0$ $5 - \underline{0} = 5$

Purpose: To discover and write the combinations that make 5; to tell oral subtraction stories about 5.

LESSON 71. Combinations That Make 5; Word Problems in Subtraction

Group Activity

Select the 5-box and have the children fill it with blocks. Point out that in the center they will find two combinations composed of neighbors, or consecutive numbers, that make 5, that is, 2 + 3 and 3 + 2. Elicit that there is no double because 5 is an odd number.

Play several of the familiar games. You might cover the box with a notebook and have the children name each combination before you draw back the notebook to reveal it. (*ExN*, p. 37, #6)

Workbook Page

A. The children complete the examples.
B. Understanding the actions that take place in a printed word problem are often difficult for children. Prepare them for comprehension of word problems by having them tell what is happening in each picture. They finish the page independently.

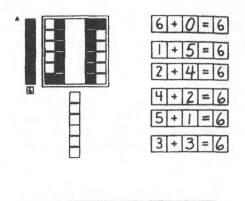

$$\boxed{6} + \boxed{0} = \boxed{6}$$
$$\boxed{1} + \boxed{5} = \boxed{6}$$
$$\boxed{2} + \boxed{4} = \boxed{6}$$
$$\boxed{4} + \boxed{2} = \boxed{6}$$
$$\boxed{5} + \boxed{1} = \boxed{6}$$
$$\boxed{3} + \boxed{3} = \boxed{6}$$

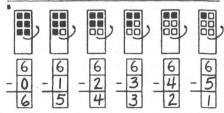

Purpose: To study the combinations that make 6 and the facts that result when subtracting numbers from 6.

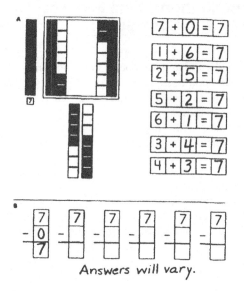

Answers will vary.

Purpose: To study the combinations that make 7 and the facts that result when subtracting numbers from 7.

LESSON 72. Combinations That Make 6; Subtracting from 6

Group Activity

The combinations that make 6 are fun to work with. The number 6 is not so big that the facts are difficult to remember. Display the 6-box and scatter two sets of blocks 1 to 5 on the table; be sure that there is only one 6-block. Have the children fill the 6-box with combinations of blocks and recite the addition fact each time; for example, "5 needs 1 to make 6." Elicit that 6 is an even number and therefore has a double in the center: 3 and 3. (*ExN*, p. 39, #10)

Contrast the combinations that make 5 with those that make 6. Set the boxes next to each other. Scatter the blocks from the 10-box and the counting board on the table. On cards write the following examples: $5 + 0 = \underline{}$, $4 + 1 = \underline{}$, $3 + 2 = \underline{}$, $2 + 3 = \underline{}$, $1 + 4 = \underline{}$, $6 + 0 = \underline{}$, $5 + 1 = \underline{}$, $4 + 2 = \underline{}$, $3 + 3 = \underline{}$, $2 + 4 = \underline{}$, and $1 + 5 = \underline{}$. Put them in a pile. A pupil draws a card (such as $6 + 0 = \underline{}$), reads it, says the answer, which tells us which box the combination of blocks belongs in, and puts it there. The box that has the most combinations can be declared the winner. (*ExN*, p. 59, #8)

Workbook Page

A. The children look at combinations of blocks and complete the equations.

B. The pattern board pictures illustrate the subtraction facts; the children complete the examples independently.

LESSON 73. Combinations That Make 7; Subtracting from 7

Group Activity

Display the 7-box and scatter the blocks on the table. Analyze the combinations as you put each one in the box. The 7-block needs nothing to make 7. Put in 1 and 6. Elicit that the reverse fact is $6 + 1$, which you place as the last combination in the box. Next comes $2 + 5 = 7$ and on the far side of the box, $5 + 2 = 7$. Stand the center combinations outside the box: $3 + 4$ and $4 + 3$. Elicit that 7 is an odd number and therefore has two combinations in the center composed of consecutive numbers; put them in the center of the box. (*ExN*, p. 40, #12)

The children need to play more games with the combinations that make 7 because these are difficult ones. Play the game Which Blocks Are Missing? When the children's eyes are closed, hide one combination of blocks from the 7-box, such as $3 + 4$. Tell them to open their eyes and ask, "Which blocks are missing?" When they have named the blocks, give them to the children to put back in the 7-box. Let the children take the role of teacher; this is an important experience for language-poor children. (*ExN*, p. 37, #5).

Workbook Page

A. The children complete the equations for the combinations that make 7.

B. They write the answers to the related subtraction facts.

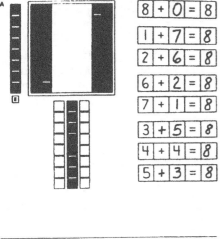

$$8 + 0 = 8$$
$$1 + 7 = 8$$
$$2 + 6 = 8$$
$$6 + 2 = 8$$
$$7 + 1 = 8$$
$$3 + 5 = 8$$
$$4 + 4 = 8$$
$$5 + 3 = 8$$

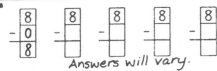

Answers will vary.

Purpose: To study the combinations that make 8 and the facts that result when subtracting numbers from 8.

LESSON 74. Combinations That Make 8; Subtracting from 8

Group Activity

Have a child build a stair in the 8-box, making each block stand up vertically. Turn the box around and have another child build a stair from 1 to 7 on the other side, going in the opposite direction. Have two children mesh together the two stairs as they recite the combinations; for example, the first child puts 7 down and says, "7 needs?" The other child touches the 1-block and answers, "1." Continue until all the combinations are lying down in the box. Elicit that 8 is even because of the double, 4 + 4. (*ExN*, p. 36, #3)

The combination 5 + 3 is one of the most difficult. Children who have trouble may find it helpful to hold out the left hand with fingers stretched out to mean 5 and then to add 3 to 5 by stretching out the thumb and 2 fingers of the right hand. Together they make 8. Roman numeral VIII is excellent for showing 5 + 3 for older pupils.

Workbook Page

A. The combinations at the top of the page are easy to see. The center double, 4 + 4, helps children recall that 3, which is smaller than 4, needs 5, which is bigger than 4. Also, 3 and 5 are both odd numbers that when added together, make the even number 8. The children complete the equations independently.

B. The children subtract from 8 independently.

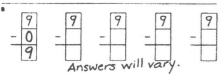

$$9 + 0 = 9$$
$$1 + 8 = 9$$
$$2 + 7 = 9$$
$$3 + 6 = 9$$
$$6 + 3 = 9$$
$$7 + 2 = 9$$
$$8 + 1 = 9$$
$$4 + 5 = 9$$
$$5 + 4 = 9$$

Answers will vary.

Purpose: To study the combinations that make 9 and the facts that result when subtracting numbers from 9.

LESSON 75. Combinations That Make 9; Subtracting from 9

Group Activity

The children should know the 10-facts very well by now. They are the most important ones in our number system, which is based on 10. They can approach the 9-facts by comparing them with the 10-facts. Place the empty 9-box next to the already filled 10-box. Tell the children that they are going to fill the 9-box by moving the blocks over from the 10-box. Elicit which block won't fit into the 9-box (the 10-block). Now have a child put the 9-block in and recite the combination 9 and 0 make 9. Have another child show that the 1-block needs the 8 block, and so on, until the 9-box has been filled. Remove the extra 9-block. Elicit that 4 + 5 and 5 + 4 in the center prove that 9 is an odd number. (*ExN*, p. 40, #12)

The following game is an excellent way to review the 9-facts and the 10-facts. The class needs enough blocks to fill both boxes completely. Divide the class into two teams. Team A fills the 10-box, while Team B fills the 9-box. Dump out all the blocks onto the table. Use a stop-and-go cube to control the turns. If a player from Team A gets "go," he or she puts one combination of blocks into the 10-box and dictates it to a scribe at the chalkboard. The teams take turns dropping the cube, filling their boxes, and dictating examples. The team that fills its box first wins.

Workbook Page

A. The combinations are easy to see. Note that 4 + 5 and 5 + 4 have been placed outside the box for emphasis. The children complete the equations independently.

B. The children complete the examples in subtracting from 9.

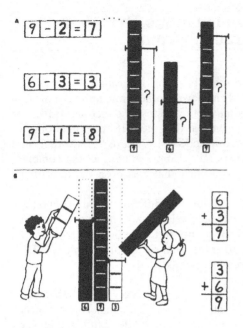

$9 - 2 = 7$

$6 - 3 = 3$

$9 - 1 = 8$

	6
+	3
	9

	3
+	6
	9

Purpose: To discover the number of an unknown block, which can be compared to a known block.

LESSON 76. Finding the Mystery Block

Group Activity
Cut a strip of white paper to fit each block from 1 to 10 and paste the strips over one side of the blocks. Choose a block such as 5 and stand it next to another block that isn't covered, perhaps 7. Elicit that the mystery block is 2 units less than 7. Have a child record it at the chalkboard, $7 - 2 = \_\_$. The children figure out that the mystery block is 5. Turn the block around as proof. Repeat the demonstration with other combinations. This kind of thinking will be used in finding X in the next book. This demonstration is excellent for children with poor language skills as it helps them organize their thinking.

Workbook Page
A. Elicit that the first equation tells us how to find the mystery block in the first pair. The children read the equation, trace the line, and identify the mystery block. Help the children complete the equation to find the mystery block in each set of blocks. They draw a line between the equation and the blocks illustrating it.

B. One of the most difficult combinations is shown. The pupils are encouraged to think in 3s: to make 9, 6 needs 3, and vice versa, 3 needs 6, which is shown as $3 + 3$.

8	5	7	5	6	0	3
+1	+2	+2	+3	+3	+8	+6
9	7	9	8	9	8	9

2	4	4	3	5	2	9
+7	+5	+3	+5	+4	+5	+0
9	9	7	8	9	7	9

9	8	7	9	9	7	9
-0	-3	-5	-8	-2	-2	-5
9	5	2	1	7	5	4

9	9	8	9	9	7	8
-7	-3	-5	-6	-4	-3	-8
2	6	3	3	5	4	0

Purpose: To test the most difficult facts with sums less than 10 in both addition and subtraction.

LESSON 77. Test: Difficult Combinations in Addition and Subtraction

Group Activity
Play an interesting game called What's My Rule? (What rule makes me choose the second block?) Scatter the blocks on the table. Stand up the 9-block and then next to it, the 8-block. Tell the children you will show them another pair of blocks. Stand up the 6-block and then the 5-block. Ask if any child can choose two blocks with the same rule in mind. If they can, ask someone to state the rule: Choose a block and then choose another block one smaller (or one less) than the first block. The following would be more difficult: 5 then 8, 6 then 9 (rule: add 3 to the first number).

Other quick reviews include playing the Hiding Game, at the same time analyzing the "story" of 9, 8, or 7 as you ask the questions: "In this hand is 8. What is in the other hand to make 9?" Next time: "In this hand is 1. What is in the other hand to make 9?"

Workbook Page
A. The children draw a line around examples with a sum of 9 (optional). This forces them to think through the test ahead of time. The children complete the examples independently.

B. Review the subtraction facts orally before children complete the examples.

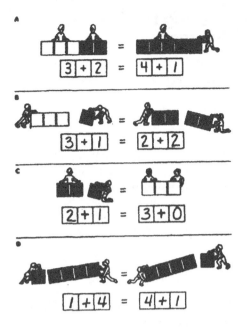

$3 + 2 = 4 + 1$

$3 + 1 = 2 + 2$

$2 + 1 = 3 + 0$

$1 + 4 = 4 + 1$

Purpose: To figure out the missing addend in a pair that equals the sum of another pair of addends.

LESSON 78. Finding Pairs of Addends That are Equal

Group Activity
Have a child fill the 5-box with combinations of blocks. Elicit that each pair of blocks is just as big as the pair next to it. Scatter the blocks on the table. Pick up two blocks that make 5. Place them end to end and announce: "I have 3 and 2." Elicit that they equal 5. Ask, "Who can get two different blocks that together are just as big as 3 and 2?" A child selects, perhaps, 4 and 1 and places them next to 3 and 2. Have another child record this on the chalkboard as $3 + 2 = 4 + 1$. Explain that we know each side equals 5, but we don't write it down. Let another child present a pair, and call on someone to find a pair whose sum will be the same (perhaps the 5-block and zero: $4 + 1 = 5 + 0$). This is a nice way to review combinations. Use other number boxes such as the 7-box or the 9-box.

Workbook Page
In the first equation the illustrations make it easy to see that $3 + 2 = 4 + 1$. In the other equations the children record the blocks they see pictured. Make sure they understand that the pair of addends on one side of the equal sign is "just as big as" the pair on the other side.

$4 + 2 = 3 + 3$

$\overset{9}{\overbrace{5 + 4}} = \overset{9}{\overbrace{7 + 2}}$

$3 + 6 = 4 + 5$

$8 + 1 = 6 + 3$

$3 + 2 = 1 + 4$

Purpose: To learn how to figure out the addend missing in a pair of addends that has the same sum as another pair of addends.

LESSON 79. Finding One Missing Addend When Two Pairs of Addends Equal Each Other

Group Activity
Finding the missing addend is more difficult when numbers without illustrations are shown. Scatter face up two sets of number markers 1 to 10 and two plus signs. Have a child select two number markers and put a plus sign between them, for example, $3 + 3$. You provide the equal sign and the first number of the other pair, thus, $3 + 3 = 5 + \underline{\quad}$. The next player must locate the missing addend that will produce the same total (6). Thus, $3 + 3 = 5 + 1$. Now the two sides of the equation are equal.

Workbook Page
After playing the game described above, children should find this page easy.

A. The illustration makes the missing addend visible.

B. The children complete the equations independently.

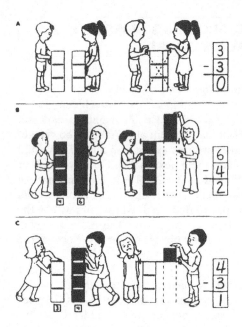

Purpose: To find the difference between the two amounts, or blocks, by subtracting the amount they have in common, which is the smaller amount.

LESSON 80. Introducing the Concept of Difference

Group Activity

Stand up two equal blocks side by side. Elicit that there is no difference between them; they are equal.

Next, stand up two unequal blocks such as the 4-block and the 6-block. Elicit that the 6-block is bigger than the 4-block, the 4-block is smaller than the 6-block, and there is a difference of 2 between them. Tell the children you will explain how we calculate the difference in written arithmetic. Demonstrate subtraction by holding your fingers around the 4-block and hiding the corresponding 4 units of the 6-block. That leaves the difference of 2 units sticking out above your fingers. Tell the children we subtract the amount that is the same, that is, the amount they have in common, which also means we take the smaller number from the larger number: $6 - 4 = 2$.

Workbook Page

A. Explain that each child has a 3-block. There is no difference: thus, $3 - 3 = 0$.

B. The children have blocks of different heights. If we take the amount they have in common from the 6-block, the difference of 2 units stands out.

C. The explanation is the same as for B. The boy holds the difference of 1 unit in his hands.

The children record these examples in the boxes provided.

LESSON 81. Finding the Difference

Group Activity

Play a game in which you pass a different number of cubes to each child (10 or fewer cubes). Select two children and have them each make a row of cubes and place them parallel to each other, for example, 6 cubes next to 9 cubes. Elicit that to find the difference between the rows you subtract the amount that is the same (6 cubes) from the 9 cubes. Do this by covering both groups of 6 cubes with a piece of paper, saying, "Up to here they are the same." This leaves the difference of 3 showing. Have the children record this on paper, $9 - 6 = 3$. Do the same with several pairs of children. In some cases there may be no difference, for example, $4 - 4 = 0$.

Workbook Page

A. Elicit that one block has 7 dolls and the other, 4 dolls. Children find the difference, $7 - 4 = 3$ as is pictured.

B. The father is 5 feet tall, the son, 3 feet. To find the difference, subtract: $5 - 3 = 2$. The father is 2 feet taller than the son.

C. The giraffe is 8 feet tall, the girl, 3 feet. How many feet taller is the giraffe? $8 - 3 = 5$. The giraffe is 5 feet taller than the girl.

Purpose: To learn how to find the difference between unequal amounts.

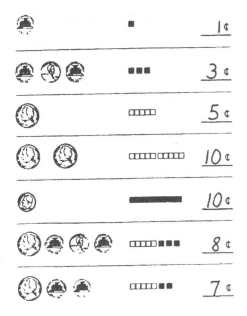

		1¢
		3¢
		5¢
		10¢
		10¢
		8¢
		7¢

Purpose: To recognize pennies, nickels, and dimes and to learn the value of each coin.

Coin Lotto Game

| 1¢ | 5¢ | 10¢ | 10¢ |

Purpose: To recognize pennies, nickels, and dimes, and to know their equivalent values.

LESSON 82. The Value of Coins

Note: The value of a coin cannot be discovered by looking at its size. Children often think the nickel, since it is larger, is worth more than a dime and therefore confuse these two coins.

To teach children the value of each coin, tape coins or pictures of coins to the blocks that represent their value. Tape a penny on each of twenty 1-cubes, a nickel on each of five 5-blocks, and a dime on each of five 10-blocks.

Some children find the concept of exchanging 5 pennies for 1 nickel difficult. When they hear that "5 pennies are in a nickel" or "5 pennies make a nickel," they can't *see* that it is true. For these literal-minded children, the model must correspond to the language.

The following experiment is worth preparing. Fashion a hollow 5-block by folding a yellow paper shield around three sides of a 5-block and close one end (see Lesson 89). Next, display five 1-cubes, each with a penny on it. Place 5 "pennies" into the hollow nickel shield. Turn over the filled nickel shield, showing the nickel pasted on the outside. Now ask, "How many pennies are in a nickel?" Have a child remove the nickel shield to reveal that there are, indeed, "5 pennies in a nickel."

Group Activity

Ask the children to build a stair from 1 to 5 from the cubes with pennies pasted on them. Show that the 5 cubes with pennies can be exchanged for and replaced by the 5-block with the nickel pasted on it. Elicit that 6¢ in this case will be 1 nickel and 1 penny. Have the children build 7¢ as 1 nickel and 2 pennies, 8¢ as 1 nickel and 3 pennies, and 9¢ as 1 nickel and 4 pennies. Ask how many nickels equal a dime. Show that 10 pennies also equal a dime.

Tell the children that the symbol ¢ stands for *cent* and that five cents is written 5¢.

Workbook Page

Go over the page orally. The children write the number that stands for each set of coins.

LESSON 83. The Value of Coins

Group Activity

First have the children sort a pile of coins into groups of like coins. Placing the coins on a piece of felt in the center of the table helps children handle the coins. Next have each pupil use page 83 in his or her workbook as a lotto card. The center pile should contain enough coins for each pupil: 6 pennies, 2 nickels, and 1 dime. Turn two sets of number markers face down on a tray (or two dice can be dropped). One child is appointed cashier. Have the children take turns selecting a number marker (or dropping two dice). If the result is 7, the player takes 7 pennies from the center supply and as a first step places 5 of the pennies on the row of 5 pennies on the lotto card. Next, the player asks the cashier for a nickel in exchange for these 5 pennies. The nickel just "purchased" and the remaining 2 pennies are placed on the pictured coins on the lotto card. As the game progresses, much exchanging goes on, guided by the model on the lotto card. The first players to fill their cards with coins are the winners. To play the next game, have the children keep the coins in place on their cards.

Play a Calling Back Game. Ask for the coins by name. For example, say, "Who has a dime?" All those who have dimes toss them into a box labeled 10¢ or with a picture of a dime on it.

Workbook Page

Go over the page orally first, discussing the value of each group of coins. Children fill in the blanks independently. If some children need more practice, repeat the games in Lessons 82 and 83.

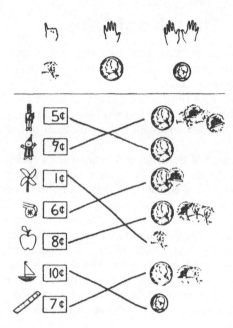

Purpose: To test the children's knowledge of the value of pennies, nickels, and dimes by having them buy items from a "store."

Group Activity

Make price tags for items that cost 10¢ or less. Label the items and display them as in a store. Each child obtains a supply of money by playing the lotto game in Lesson 83. The children take turns picking out an item they can afford and "paying" for it. Many penny items are a help at the end of the game. Children very much enjoy playing store.

Provide practice in oral work by giving each child a supply of coins and then holding up an item. Announce, for example, "This sticker is worth 7¢. What coins can you use to buy it?" Then have them "buy" it.

Workbook Page

Children connect the price tags with the correct coin(s). They finish the page independently.

Purpose. To teach the children how to subtract one amount of money from another. This is the foundation for learning to make change.

LESSON 85. How Much Money Is Left?

Group Activity

Give several children 10 pennies each. Display a toy that costs less than 10¢. Elicit whether one of the children has enough money to pay for it. Ask the class how much money will be left. Call on someone to write the subtraction example on the chalkboard, for example, $10 - 7 = 3$. Then have the child pay for the item and state how much she or he has left (3¢).

In the next game give each child a dime. Show a toy that costs 5¢. Elicit that the child must exchange the dime for 2 nickels and spend 1 nickel to buy the toy. Have the children record the example on the chalkboard as a simple subtraction example, $10 - 5 = 5$. Explain that this is the number work, that the final amount must be written again using the ¢ sign as a label: 5¢.

Workbook Page

Go over the page orally first.

A. Elicit that the child has a dime and wants to buy a candy cane for 5¢. Elicit that the dime is worth 10¢. The arithmetic is written in the example to the right. The children finish the example and then write the answer again next to the ¢ sign on the space provided.

The children finish the page independently.

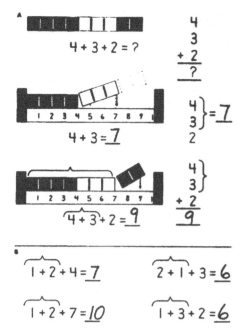

4 + 3 + 2 = ?

$\begin{array}{r} 4 \\ 3 \\ + 2 \\ \hline ? \end{array}$

4 + 3 = _7_

$\left.\begin{array}{r} 4 \\ 3 \\ 2 \end{array}\right\} = \underline{7}$

$\overbrace{4 + 3} + 2 = \underline{9}$

$\left.\begin{array}{r} 4 \\ 3 \\ + 2 \\ \hline 9 \end{array}\right.$

$\overbrace{1 + 2} + 4 = \underline{7}$ $\overbrace{2 + 1} + 3 = \underline{6}$

$\overbrace{1 + 2} + 7 = \underline{10}$ $\overbrace{1 + 3} + 2 = \underline{6}$

Purpose: To learn to solve addition examples with more than two addends.

3¢   2¢   5¢

(3 + 2) + 5 = _10_   _10_¢

$\boxed{4} + \boxed{3} + \boxed{2} = \boxed{9}$ _9_ ¢

4¢   3¢   2¢

$\boxed{5} + \boxed{2} + \boxed{2} = \boxed{9}$ _9_ ¢

5¢   2¢   2¢

$\boxed{2} + \boxed{6} + \boxed{1} = \boxed{9}$ _9_ ¢

2¢   6¢   1¢

Purpose: To help children solve problems in which the prices of three items must be added to get the total cost.

LESSON 86. Adding Three Numbers

Note: It is impossible to add more than two numbers at a time. The addition of several addends must be done step by step. Adding 2 + 3 + 4 = ___ must be solved in two steps. The first step is 2 + 3 = 5; the second is 5 + 4 = 9. The total is 9.

Group Activity

Explain that we cannot add more than two numbers, or addends, at a time. However, examples can have more than two addends. Write such an example on the chalkboard: 3 + 3 + 2 = ___. Have a child place two 3-blocks and one 2-block end to end. Elicit that the first two blocks make 6; replace them with a 6-block. Now the children can easily add 6 + 2 = 8.

Play a Hiding Game. Hide three blocks behind your back, such as 3 and 5 and 2. Say, "I have three blocks that make 10 altogether. In one hand I have 3 and 5. What is in the other hand?" Have a child write this addition example on the chalkboard. Remind them to keep the sum of the first two numbers in their heads and then to add the last number to it to get the total.

Workbook Page

A. Go over the examples. On the chalkboard show that in either equation form or column addition, the first two addends are added and then the third is added to that partial sum.

B. The children finish the page independently.

LESSON 87. Finding the Total Cost

Group Activity

Group together three items whose price labels total 10¢ or less, for instance, 3¢, 2¢, and 5¢. Have a child place end to end the corresponding blocks with coins on top: 3 pennies, 2 pennies, and 1 nickel. Elicit that you add 3 and 2, keep the sum in mind, and then add 5 and 5 to get the total, 10. Have a child write the example on the chalkboard in equation form. Put brackets around the first two numbers to be added together. Remind the children to write the answer (10) once again with the cent sign, 10¢.

Workbook Page

A. Elicit that each example shows three articles that are to be bought and that in each case the children are to find the total cost. The price of each toy is to be written as one of the addends in the equation.

B. The children find the sum and then in the space provided write the answer again next to the cent sign.

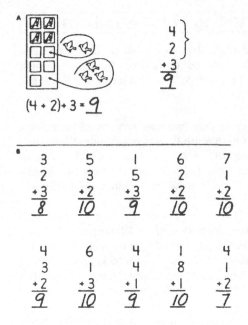

$(4 + 2) + 3 = 9$

3	5	1	6	7
2	3	5	2	1
+3	+2	+3	+2	+2
8	10	9	10	10

4	6	4	1	4
3	1	4	8	1
+2	+3	+1	+1	+2
9	10	9	10	7

Purpose: To test the addition of three numbers.

LESSON 88. Test: Addition of Three Numbers

Group Activity
Write several examples on the chalkboard. Have children bracket the two numbers they will add first to get the partial sum. They then add the partial sum and the third addend to find the total. Remind children that the order of the addends in addition can be changed without changing the sum. Use the 10-box. Put in the 2-block, the 5-block, and the 3-block to complete the row. Have a child write this on the chalkboard in column form: $2 + 5 + 3 = 10$. Change the order of the blocks to $2 + 3 + 5$ and have the children explain that the sum is the same even though the order of the addends has been changed.

Workbook Page
A. Go over the story problem orally.
B. The children finish the test independently.

5

$5 - 3 = 2$

$4 - 3 = 1$

$7 - 6 = 1$

$7 - 3 = 4$

$5 - 2 = 3$

Purpose: To use subtraction shields as another way to teach subtraction.

LESSON 89. Concept Shown by Subtraction Shields

Note: Subtraction shields can be made from paper or card stock and then colored. Each shield corresponds in size and color to its corresponding number block. Cut out a three-sided shield that fits over a block. One end is left open and the other end closed by pasting two flaps together. The shields can be slipped over any number block to cover the units subtracted.

Group Activity
Hold up a 5-block and explain that you can't chop off 3 units, or cubes. Show that you *can* cover up 3 units of the 5-block with the 3-shield to show you are subtracting them. The child sees that 2 units remain visible. Demonstrate with other blocks and shields.

Line up the shields in sequence from 1 to 10. Put each number block in the counting board. Give the children turns covering each block with a shield that will leave only 1 unit showing, or a remainder of 1. The facts that result will be: $10 - 9 = 1$; $9 - 8 = 1$; $8 - 7 = 1, \ldots 2 - 1 = 1$.

Workbook Page
A. The children see 5 lions. The pictured subtraction shield indicates that 3 are hidden. The children write the answer in the box on the right.
B. The children complete the equations independently.

8	10	5	7	9	6	10
+2	-2	+1	+3	-0	+1	-4
10	8	6	10	9	7	6

10	10	9	6	8	10	10
-7	-5	+1	+4	-8	+0	-1
3	5	10	10	0	10	9

1	10	6	5	10	5	4
+9	-9	-1	+5	-10	+0	+6
10	1	5	10	0	5	10

3	10	10	0	2	10	7
+7	-6	-8	+9	+8	-3	-6
10	4	2	9	10	7	1

Purpose: To test mastery of the following groups of facts in addition and subtraction: the 10-facts, +0, −0, +1, −1, remainder of 0, remainder of 1.

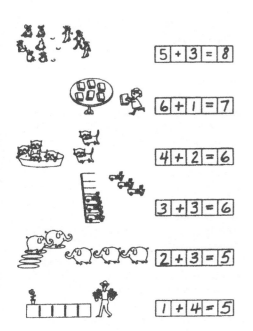

Purpose: To analyze and solve problems in finding the sum.

Note: To solve problems, children must be able to determine which operation is required, addition or subtraction. This book has presented pictured problems that the children state in their own words and then record in symbols. To review addition in problem solving see Lessons 23 to 28, 78, 79, and 86 to 88.

LESSON 90. Mastery Test A in Addition and Subtraction

Note: The tests on pages 90, 92, and 94 may be thought of as a net in which to catch errors that the children make in addition and subtraction. Analyze errors by noting in which group of structurally related facts the wrong examples belong. The relevant groups should be reviewed before giving each test again. The groups in this test were taught in the following lessons: 10-facts in addition (Lessons 18 to 27), 10-facts in subtraction (Lessons 28 to 35), adding 0 and adding 1 (Lessons 36 to 39), and subtracting 0 and subtracting 1 (Lessons 48 to 55).

Group Activity

Play this game to review the 10-facts in addition. Give each child a strip of paper the size of the 10-block (7½ inches by 1 inch). Make cards for the relevant addition facts in equation form. Scatter the blocks from the 10-box in the center of the table. Hold up one of the addition cards, perhaps 7 + 3 = ___. The first child reads the equation, places the corresponding blocks on his or her 10-strip, and states the whole equation. The other children do the same with other equations. They all keep their combinations of blocks to play a subtraction game in a similar way.

Workbook Page

The children look over the test. Elicit that the main part of the test is on the 10-facts; there are ten addition facts and ten subtraction facts. The children ring each addition fact that makes 10. Then they ring each subtraction fact. They will find that all twenty facts are there. Go over the test orally first. The children complete the test independently.

LESSON 91. Problems in Finding the Sum

Group Activity

Invent word problems for the children and have them use the blocks to demonstrate the action that takes place. Try not to use verbal cues (such as "how many in all?") as this prevents children from thinking through the entire problem. For example, say, "There are 3 birds eating crumbs (child gets the 3-block) and 4 more birds fly in to join them (child adds the 4-block to the 3-block). How many birds are eating crumbs now?" Elicit that there are more in the end, so the problem is solved by addition, 3 + 4 = 7. Have several children write this example at the chalkboard and write the answer with its label, 7 birds.

Next have children take turns telling their own addition stories. Make sure the sums are 10 or less.

Some children, when hearing a word problem, cannot visualize what took place. Try playing the Screen Game. Begin by filling the 4-board with cubes, and then move it behind a screen where the children can hear some action being performed on it. When the pattern reappears, a child says, "I see 6 cubes." Ask the child "Did I add cubes or did I take cubes away?" The child says, "Added 2 cubes," records this with 4 + 2, and then completes the entire equation: 4 + 2 = 6. (*ExN*, p. 54, #12)

Workbook Page

Call on a child to explain the problem shown in the first picture: "There are 5 campers sitting around a fire and 3 more campers come. How many campers are there now?" Ask the child to state the example, 5 + 3 = 8, and put the answer in context, "There are 8 campers." Go over the other problems orally. The children complete the page independently.

$$\begin{array}{ccccccc} 4 & 6 & 0 & 6 & 2 & 5 & 8 \\ +2 & -4 & +2 & +2 & -0 & +3 & -6 \\ \hline 6 & 2 & 2 & 8 & 2 & 8 & 2 \end{array}$$

$$\begin{array}{ccccccc} 6 & 9 & 7 & 0 & 4 & 1 & 3 \\ -2 & -7 & +2 & +3 & -2 & +2 & -2 \\ \hline 4 & 2 & 9 & 3 & 2 & 3 & 1 \end{array}$$

$$\begin{array}{ccccccc} 2 & 9 & 8 & 5 & 8 & 2 & 5 \\ +7 & -2 & -3 & +3 & -2 & +6 & +2 \\ \hline 9 & 7 & 5 & 8 & 6 & 8 & 7 \end{array}$$

$$\begin{array}{ccccccc} 3 & 7 & 5 & 2 & 2 & 8 & 7 \\ +5 & -5 & -2 & +4 & +5 & -5 & -2 \\ \hline 8 & 2 & 3 & 6 & 7 & 3 & 5 \end{array}$$

Purpose: To test mastery of the following groups of facts in addition and subtraction: adding 2 to a number, subtracting 2 from a number, a remainder of 2, zero facts, and the combinations $5+3$, $3+5$, $8-3$, and $8-5$.

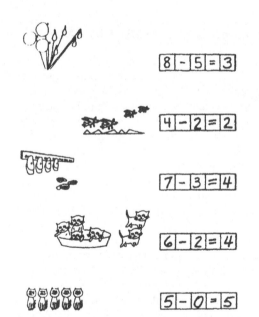

Purpose: To learn how to solve problems in finding the remainder.

LESSON 92. Mastery Test B in Addition and Subtraction

Note: The groups of structurally related facts on this test should be reviewed first, as they are difficult facts. The groups were originally introduced in the following lessons of this book: adding 2 to a number (Lessons 40 to 47), subtracting 2 from a number (Lessons 50 to 54), a remainder of 2 (Lesson 53), and combinations made from the component parts 5 and 3 (Lesson 74).

Group Activity

The children should be familiar with adding and subtracting 2 from odd and even numbers. The Sticker Game is a good review using written examples (Lesson 47). The children look at an example that tells them under which board a sticker has been hidden. A card with $5+2=\underline{\quad}$ tells them to look under the 7-board to find the prize. Adding 0 and subtracting 0 should be included.

Difficult examples with a remainder of 2 can be practiced in a game of Slap Jack (see Lesson 55). The children learn to distinguish at a glance between examples with a remainder of 1 (pairs of consecutive numbers) and those with a remainder of 2 (pairs of consecutive odd or even numbers).

Workbook Page

The children look over the test. They ring the examples with a remainder of 2 and put a special mark by the examples $5+3$, $3+5$, $8-3$, and $8-5$ (optional). They finish the test independently.

LESSON 93. Problems in Finding the Remainder

Note: It is important for children to see the opposite nature of addition and subtraction. Therefore, begin with a few addition stories. Elicit that in each story the original number got bigger, or increased. Then explain that in today's problems the beginning number is going to get smaller, or become less. The solution will be found by subtraction. To review subtraction in problem solving see Lessons 28 to 35, 50, 51, 66, and 71 to 89.

Group Activity

Fill pattern boards 1 to 10 with cubes and pass them out to the children. Tell a subtraction story, for instance, "I bought 8 peaches; on the way home I ate 2 of them. How many peaches were in the bag when I got home?" The child with the 8-board should recognize that she or he is the one who has the right amount to demonstrate the story and says, "I have 8 peaches. I ate 2 (removes 2 cubes). I have 6 peaches left." Elicit that the number of peaches became less, so the problem was solved by subtraction. Ask another child to write the example on the chalkboard, $8-2=6$, and to state the answer in context, 6 peaches.

Have the children take turns making up subtraction stories that they can demonstrate with their cubes and pattern boards. Choose a child to write the subtraction examples on the chalkboard. The children should realize that the *action* in the situation determines the use of subtraction to solve the problems, not memorized word clues. For children who find subtraction difficult, play the Screen Game described in Lessons 32 and 63. (*ExN*, p. 54, #11, #12)

Workbook Page

Call on a child to explain the story shown in the first picture. Elicit that since there were fewer good balloons in the end, the problem will be solved by a subtraction example, which is already written to the right. The children can see that 3 good balloons remain, $8-5=3$. Go over the rest of the problems orally if necessary. The children finish the page independently.

$$\begin{array}{ccccccc} 3 & 5 & 4 & 6 & 8 & 5 & 2 \\ +2 & -3 & +4 & +3 & -4 & +4 & -1 \\ \hline 5 & 2 & 8 & 9 & 4 & 9 & 1 \end{array}$$

$$\begin{array}{ccccccc} 9 & 3 & 3 & 2 & 6 & 4 & 9 \\ -3 & -2 & +3 & +1 & -3 & +3 & -5 \\ \hline 6 & 1 & 6 & 3 & 3 & 7 & 4 \end{array}$$

$$\begin{array}{ccccccc} 1 & 7 & 9 & 4 & 9 & 2 & 3 \\ +0 & -4 & -6 & +5 & -4 & +2 & +6 \\ \hline 1 & 3 & 3 & 9 & 5 & 4 & 9 \end{array}$$

$$\begin{array}{ccccccc} 3 & 4 & 4 & 1 & 2 & 7 & 5 \\ +4 & -2 & -4 & +1 & +3 & -3 & -2 \\ \hline 7 & 2 & 0 & 2 & 5 & 4 & 3 \end{array}$$

Purpose: To test mastery of the following groups of facts, both addition and subtraction: the doubles, the odd numbers, and the combinations $6 + 3$, $3 + 6$, $9 - 3$, and $9 - 6$.

Note: Review these groups of structurally related facts before giving the test: the doubles in addition (Lessons 56 and 58), the doubles in subtraction (Lessons 60, 62, 64, and 65), the odd numbers (or addition of consecutive numbers) (Lessons 57 and 59), subtraction from odd numbers (Lessons 61, 63, 64, and 65), and the combinations $6 + 3$, $3 + 6$, $9 - 3$, and $9 - 6$ (Lessons 75 and 77).

$$10 - 5 = 5$$

$$4 + 1 = 5$$

$$3 + 4 = 7$$

$$6 - 3 = 3$$

$$4 - 3 = 1$$

Purpose: To demonstrate the ability to recognize a given problem as one of finding the sum or the remainder.

Group Activity

The pattern boards are the most easily remembered representation of even and odd numbers and the facts that can be demonstrated with them. A good review is a game played with two paper cups, each of which is filled with cubes representing an addend and which is then dumped out on a table. As one cup is emptied, the child calls out "3" and when the other cup is emptied, "and 4 make 7," and then puts the cubes into the right pattern board.

The following is a good review of written facts. Paste on the faces of dominoes or print on small cards the following ten addition examples for the odd numbers:

$$\begin{array}{cccccccccc} 1 & 0 & 2 & 1 & 3 & 2 & 4 & 3 & 5 & 4 \\ +0 & +1 & +1 & +2 & +2 & +3 & +3 & +4 & +4 & +5 \end{array}$$

Arrange the pattern boards in sequence from 1 to 10. Time the children as they sort out the examples and place them beneath the appropriate patterns. The same game can be played with the related subtraction examples.

$$\begin{array}{cccccccccc} 9 & 9 & 7 & 7 & 5 & 5 & 3 & 3 & 1 & 1 \\ -5 & -4 & -4 & -3 & -3 & -2 & -2 & -1 & -1 & -0 \end{array}$$

Workbook Page

The children put an X over each double and each subtraction from an even number. They ring the combinations that result from adding two consecutive numbers and each of the related subtraction facts. They locate the difficult combinations in addition, $6 + 3$ and $3 + 6$, and the related subtraction facts, $9 - 3$ and $9 - 6$. Then they finish the page independently.

LESSON 95. Mastery Test in Solving Problems in Addition and Subtraction

Oral Test in Problem Solving

Put away all the materials and give each child pencil and paper, preferably with boxes printed in which they can record the equations.

Now tell number stories. The children write an equation for each story and ring the answer. Here are a few suggestions:

1. The teacher took 3 girls and 2 boys to the zoo. How many children did the teacher take to the zoo?
2. There were 6 seals on a rock. 4 slid off and swam away. How many seals were left on the rock?
3. There were 2 big lions in one cage and 4 small lions in another cage. How many lions did the keeper have to feed?
4. Betsy went to see the bears. There were 7 bears in the beginning but 3 went back into caves. How many bears could she still see?

Workbook Page

Explain that these problems are to be solved by addition or subtraction. The children should look carefully at each picture to find out what is being asked for and how to find the answer. They then complete the equation to the right of each picture. If children have trouble solving problems, play more of the review games in Lessons 91 and 93.

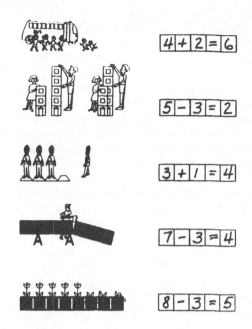

$4 + 2 = 6$

$5 - 3 = 2$

$3 + 1 = 4$

$7 - 3 = 4$

$8 - 3 = 5$

Purpose: To demonstrate the ability to recognize a given problem as one of finding the sum, finding the remainder, or finding the difference.

LESSON 96. Mastery Test in Solving Problems in Addition and Subtraction

Note: It is easy for children to distinguish between problems in which something becomes more in the end from those in which something becomes less, or decreases. Before giving this test review the more difficult task of finding the difference. To find the difference, two numbers are compared and then the smaller number is subtracted from the larger number. Review Lessons 80 and 81.

Oral Test in Problem Solving

Put away all the materials and give each child a pencil and paper, preferably with boxes printed in which to write equations.

Here are a few suggestions. (You may want to make up more problems.)

1. Terry has 5 marbles. Chris has 7 marbles. What is the difference between their piles of marbles?
2. There are 9 dogs walking in the park. Their owners take 4 of the dogs home. How many dogs are in the park now?
3. There are 10 cars parked at the supermarket. Then 2 cars leave. Now how many cars are parked at the supermarket?
4. Roberto had 8 books. He got 2 more books for his birthday. How many books does Roberto have now?

Workbook Page

Explain that there are three kinds of problems to be solved on this page—problems in addition and subtraction, and problems of finding the difference. The children should look carefully at each picture to find out what is being asked and how to find the answer. Then they write the equation in the boxes provided at the right.

Made in the USA
Las Vegas, NV
20 September 2023

77854966R00037